THE FIRST
FOUR DAYS

THE FIRST FOUR DAYS

The Creation of the Universe: an Annotated Account

DELMAR DOBBERPUHL

WinePressPublishing
Great Books, Defined.

WinePress Publishing (PO Box 428, Enumclaw, WA 98022) functions only as book publisher. As such, the ultimate design, content, editorial accuracy, and views expressed or implied in this work are those of the author.

Unless otherwise noted, all Scriptures are taken from the *New American Standard Bible*, © 1960, 1963, 1968, 1971, 1972, 1973, 1975, 1977 by The Lockman Foundation. Used by permission.

Scripture references marked KJV are taken from the *King James Version* of the Bible.

ISBN 13: 978-1-4141-2110-9
ISBN 10: 1-4141-2110-5
Library of Congress Catalog Card Number: 2011930218

Contents

Acknowledgments

THE ILLUSTRATIONS IN this book were done by a very special friend, Gene Smith, of Dewey, AZ. After he retired from his regular income job, he has become a commercial artist. He specializes in drawings and paintings of animals, both in portraits and in their natural environments. This book would be much less interesting without his dedicated effort.

I also acknowledge the initial editing of the chapters by Frank DeRemer of Santa Cruz, CA. He has great command of language structure and syntax. It is his editing that has allowed me to say what I mean in the least amount of words.

I would also like to thank all my early reviewers. They were friends and relatives who took time out of their normal activities to read and comment on what I had written.

List of Illustrations

Foreword

THE CHAPTERS IN this book were first written for a book that would have presented both a literary and a scientific exposé of the creating-and-making account (CMA) provided in Genesis 1:1–2:4a. Originally there were three of us who co-authored a viewpoint article for the *Journal of Creation* titled "Days 1–4." It can be found in Volume 21(3) 2007 on pages 69–76 of that journal. In that article we described our new position on what the CMA reported for the first four days of creation week. However, my coauthors, who would have written the literary exposé, have indefinitely delayed the completion of their task. It was our joint opinion that the presentation of the scientific exposé included in this book could not wait. The scientific material presented here is based on current knowledge of the physical universe surrounding mankind, but that knowledge changes almost daily as new discoveries are made.

We limited this book to the creating and making of the physical aspects of the universe. We do not include the spiritual aspects of creation such as the angels and the spiritual heavens that God created for them. They could easily be included in the merism "the heavens and the earth" of Genesis 1:1. Their inclusion there would be supported by the statement in Revelation 4:11: "for You created all things, and because of Your will they existed, and were created." Also the author of Genesis 2:1 reported that everything that exists in the heavens and on Earth was created and/ or made in the first six days. But creation of the non-physical aspects of the world would not be a topic that a scientist could study or analyze.

Each chapter of this book, except the first and the last, has the same basic structure. First, there are several paragraphs tying a new divine act by God to his previous acts. This includes a short summary that introduces the miracle to be described in the chapter. We then cite references to the new miracle from other places in the Bible and explain their significance. Then we introduce new scientific terminology that is related to the miracle and its products. Following this, we construct a new portion of the creating-and-making model (CM-model) based on the physical concepts provided in the CMA and complementary biblical and scientific material. The model extension is then followed by several paragraphs providing scientific evidence that supports it. Finally, a summary of the material presented in the chapter is provided.

Hence the outline of the intermediate chapters is:

The Next Miracle
Extra-CMA Biblical Descriptions
Additional Scientific Terminology
Additional Facet of the CM-Model
Supporting Scientific Evidence
Summary

An appendix has been added to provide the author's exegesis of the verses from the CMA that formed the basis of the material covered. The verses are presented as a story instead of a translation because the author is not an expert in the Hebrew language. It provides information on transliterated Hebrew words of the original Masoretic text, and their translation that was obtained from various sources. This was done so that as little as possible of the CMA author's intent would be lost in translation. Parts of the story differ from generally accepted translations such as the King James Version (KJV), New International Version (NIV) and the New American Standard Bible (NASB). This was done to add clarification rather than modify the Hebrew text or its content. It is left to the reader to determine from the context whether this story reasonably follows the Hebrew text and contains only information available from it.

Introduction

PURPOSE

THIS BOOK ATTEMPTS to explain in modern scientific terminology and recently developed physical concepts the series of events that are described in the first nineteen verses of the Creating-and-Making Account (CMA) in Genesis chapter 1. A model is constructed from these concepts, called the CM-model. The model was designed to follow directly the series of miraculous events outlined by the CMA for rapidly making and maturing all elements of the universe formed in the first four days.

We believe the words God gave mankind in the CMA that described his acts of creating and making the entire universe are the whole truth in outline form. Mankind's understanding of the universe may have changed the interpretation of those words for better or worse. In recent times, new understanding about mankind's physical environment has come almost exclusively from the physical sciences. The data scientists have collected, and especially the interpretations they have produced explaining those data, contain that new understanding. All evolutionary and even many recent creation models of the origin of the universe are based on such data and interpretations. Many of those models have assumed millions and billions of years of natural development. Theistic evolutionists, progressive creationists, and others have gone so far as to reinterpret the CMA text to make it fit their preconceived naturalistic models.

In contrast, the purpose of this book is to present a model that follows what the CMA actually says, as well as providing speculation on what it does not say. We look at the words of the text from a scientific viewpoint and build a model that fits within the context of the CMA. The CM-model involves a large amount of material that the CMA never mentions directly. However, this material was deduced from what the CMA does say and from a current understanding of the final product: the universe that mankind experience today. The author believes that this material provides insight beyond those words God gave to mankind. Such deductions were added so that the reader can relate the words God provided to terms and concepts modern scientists use today in discussions of the origin of the universe. The scientific study of the origin of the universe is called cosmology.

The CMA obviously described the origin of the same universe as that studied by cosmological scientists who support evolution. Just as obviously, we find their analyses and interpretation of their findings differ significantly from the truth of the story told in the CMA. This occurs because they rely on natural processes alone and reject God's presence at the beginning and his work to make a fully mature universe.

The Nature of the Material Presented

Some physical concepts presented in this book are highly speculative, just as all cosmology is, because no human being was there to experience and report on it. Speculation is required because scientists are all human and mankind's knowledge and understanding of the origin of natural processes will always be deficient by just studying the finished product. But, if the CM-model proposed fits God's Word without modifying it, the model certainly is worth consideration and is likely closer to what actually happened than models that are at odds with the CMA.

No one but God knows all the intelligent design that is waiting to be found in the almost boundless expanse of space external to the planet Earth and in the complexity internal to the world in which humans live. Only supernatural actions or miracles can explain how this world was created and made. Natural processes, as we know them today, were one of the products of that initial creating and making, not the ultimate cause.

The main premise we follow is that everything mankind have learned about this world was designed and built into it during creation week by an Intelligent Designer and Almighty Creator from nothing that now exists (see Hebrews 11:3 and Revelation 4:11). This is directly opposed to materialistic theories of origins (e.g., Big Bang, Steady State, Hyper-dimensional, etc.), which all include in their initial conditions something (in place of God) from which the now-known universe was formed by natural processes over long time periods.

Evolutionary theories all miss the point that without God's action in creating the natural processes that mankind can observe, these processes would never have existed. A physical process could neither design itself nor naturally select its own characteristics but must blindly follow a law set down by the ultimate designer and lawgiver—the Creator God.

Creating and Making Defined

This book is limited to the creating and making of the physical universe because that corresponds to what cosmological scientists are trying to determine: how the universe got here. We define an act of creation as bringing something into existence from nothing. *Scientists cannot study acts of creation, only their product.* The act of making is defined as the transformation of a pre-existing substance into something new and different. Creating is always miraculous. Making, in regard to the origin of the universe in only six days, is also a miracle. Only God could have performed these miracles.

For each day of creating and making, God reported the key actions he took, totaling twelve divine actions or commands. Three of the commands (Gen. 1:24, 28, 29–30) were not acts of creating or making but gave blessings and instructions to his living creatures. In the chapters that follow, we deal with the six actions God used to make the majority of the universe in the first four days. They were acts of making and rapid maturing that we call transformations. The actions of making and/or creating the living creatures on days five and six are left for another book. These creatures were created mature and required no rapid maturing.

We infer that God completed the rapid maturing of the universe by the end of the fourth day.

One must accept a creative act by faith in the Creator and his report in the CMA alone. Likewise a miraculous act of transforming will make sense only if it is accepted by faith. For each act of transformation, however, the CMA recorded preexisting materials and conditions followed by the final products under new conditions. These are reported either explicitly or by implication. In this book we identify some of the scientific evidence that has been discovered—and still remains in the universe today—and that can be interpreted as residues of those divine actions of transforming.

The acts of transforming, in the sequence presented by the CMA, are described using known physical concepts sometimes applied in speculative ways. They have been added to better translate God's words into modern scientific terminology. This speculative material is not found in previous theological literature because it has been deduced from more recent scientific data. The speculations are intended to fill in what God does not specifically report, to provide insight into what the CMA does say. They go beyond what is reported in the CMA but were carefully selected not to contradict what the CMA says. They should be considered complementary to it.

Sources for the Complementary Material

Some of the complementary material presented came from verses or passages in other books of the Bible that refer to events during creation week. Those sources provide additional information for a more detailed creation model than the CMA alone allows. They gave us further insight into the miracles God performed during creation week and how the scientific evidence could be interpreted to relate to the transformations.

The second source of complementary information was scientific literature that covers almost all aspects of mankind's scientific knowledge of the universe in the form of science textbooks and published journal articles. The sciences that have provided this information include astronomy, physics, chemistry, biology, and geology.

Limits of the CM-Model

The author realizes that all models developed to explain the origin of the universe have limitations. This is due to the finite knowledge of any individual or group of individuals that developed the model. There are portions of any model that will require change as knowledge is gained of certain aspects of the created universe.

Also, the text of the CMA was extraordinarily brief and likely allows more than one creation model. To keep the book at a reasonable length and make the model easier to understand, only our own CM-model is presented in its entirety. Alternative models are not discussed in detail even when mentioned. The reader should consider the CM-model as an example of what fits the CMA and not as the only true model. It resulted from an attempt first to determine the proper interpretation of the verses—what the author intended—and then to propose a physical model that fits. Thus, the CM-model was designed first to fit the CMA and secondly, in its light, to suggest proper interpretation of applicable current and future scientific data. This emphasizes the truth in the story told by the CMA. It is left to the reader to generate an alternative model when he finds a problem with the CM-model and does not agree with it.

WHAT IS A MIRACLE?

Creation week included a series of miracles performed by God. Therefore, a physical characterization of a miracle would be helpful in understanding the CMA. Throughout the Bible many examples of miracles are reported. A look at a broad sample of these suggested that each is a supernatural change to the existing physical world. No physical evidence remained to indicate how God performed the miracle. A sample list of such miracles includes both Old and New Testament references, e.g., Exodus 7:1–9:35, 14:21, 15:25; 1 Kings 17:22; 1 Kings 18:38; Matthew 8:3,13,15; Mark 7:34–35; Luke 8:55; John 2:7–8; John 6:21.

The main point to remember is that mankind and their science cannot explain miracles when only natural processes and physical laws are assumed without any supernatural component being involved. In physical terms, miracles are identified by a supernatural change in one or more of the three basic components of the universe: space, material substance, and time. God created all three of these with his first command for the universe to come into existence (Gen. 1:1). These components are so basic to everything physical that exists that only God can change them.

In every miracle reported in the Bible, one or more of these basic components of nature are changed. Space is changed by objects moving in a supernatural way like the sea parting for Moses as described in Exodus 14:21. Material substance is changed from one type to another like water into wine as described in John 2:7–9. Time is changed when natural processes are accelerated to supernatural rates as demonstrated by the healing of a leper as described in Matthew 8:3. And all these things are done without causing a major disruption in the physical universe.

The misunderstanding of, or failure to comprehend, this concept that God can change even these basic components of our universe has led physical scientists to postulate the almost infinite timeline apparent in their evolutionary cosmologies. But a general rule should be applied concerning a miraculous event. When God gave a command himself or worked his will through his angels or prophets, a supernatural event occurred that cannot be explained by natural processes alone.

THE CREATION WEEK TIMELINE

The important timeline to follow during creation week is the one provided in the CMA by the Creator himself. He specifically reported what he did for each of the seven days. This timeline implied that all physical concepts used to explain creating-and-making events during that formative week must fit within the days reported. For the three creating events, this was easy to explain because they happened instantaneously and may have left no physical evidence except the product. By definition of *create*, something cannot partially exist for a while, because one moment it does not exist and the next it does. For the six making or transforming events we will describe in this book, however, time probably was involved, and evidence of these miracles likely was left behind. If evidence was left, it could easily be misinterpreted without the supernatural element of the miracle being considered. From the short timeline given in the CMA, all of the mature results reported would have occurred much faster than scientists can understand based on natural process rates that exist today.

The point to ponder is: if a physical process known to occur today at a certain rate does not fit his timeline, God could have used a supernatural action involving an accelerated natural process or an entirely different process. Either way this would have been miraculous because it showed God used time, space, and material substance as tools to meet his purpose after creating them.

To scientists looking at any evidence that remains, which is all that can be observed, the result of a miracle may appear the same as results from a natural process observed today. A majority of these scientists have assumed it took as long a period of time for the mature results to occur as that natural process would take at today's rates. This false assumption has led to the large cosmological and geological ages found in almost all scientific literature today.

In the following chapters of this book, God's miraculous actions are modeled in the form of accelerated processes to fit physical processes into his timeline where the CMA requires them. This follows from the main premise of this book that God created physical processes, and he controlled their use during that first week that fulfilled his purpose and timeline. He provided his Word to mankind so that they would realize what he had done in order to provide us with a fully mature universe to live in.

CHAPTER 2

Divine Action 1: Creating the Raw Materials from Nothing

DAY 1A: EVENING—ALL IN DARKNESS

THE AUTHOR OF the CMA reported that on the first day, the Intelligent Designer, Creator, and Maker God began implementing his plan for building a physical habitat for mankind. In beginning his work, God's first action or miracle provided all the raw materials needed to make the physical universe and prepare it for living creatures in the next four days. This first miracle resulted in two physical items existing where nothing existed before: the primordial heavens (not the star-filled heavens) and the primordial earth (not the planet but a universal substance). The word earth will be capitalized when it refers to the planet mankind inhabit.

Primordial is used here to express the originally created nature of the physical heavens and earth. This original nature changed greatly in the next four days. Besides these two items, it is reasonable to infer from the words *in the beginning* that with the same divine action, God created and started the intangible physical item called *time*. Genesis 1:5 further supports this inference, where it was reported that the first day started in the evening: the beginning of the first night.

These original physical creations answer the three basic questions that cosmogony addresses. They tell the reader when, where, and what was created. The time was at the very beginning of this universe, the place was the primordial heavens, and the substance was the primordial earth. The scientific study of the creating and making of the universe from these raw materials can be called creation cosmology.

The true creation cosmology and any derived creation model must start with these three items, since nothing else physical existed before this creative act, and only they existed right after it. Any creation model should consistently follow the CMA on what God did with these raw materials to build the inhabitable universe for his living creatures. Scientific data—interpreted correctly—support such a model. The finished product at the end of the sixth day was truly a perfectly designed and completely built universe that mankind still do not fully understand or appreciate.

OTHER BIBLICAL REFERENCES TO MIRACLE 1

Psalm 103:19–22

> *The LORD has established His throne in the heavens, and his sovereignty rules over all. Bless the LORD, you His angels, mighty in strength, who perform His word, obeying the voice of His word! Bless the LORD, all you His hosts, you who serve Him, doing His will. Bless the LORD, all you works of His, in all places of His dominion; bless the LORD, O my soul!*
>
> —Ps. 103:19–22

These verses are part of the theme of a psalm or hymn that praises God for his grace and mercy toward his people. This theme is expressed in verses 1–2 of the psalm: "Bless the LORD, O my soul, and all that is within me, bless His holy name. Bless the LORD, O my soul, and forget none of His benefits." Indeed, the whole psalm consists of benefits for which to praise God. They are the benefits mankind have received from their Creator and Maker that should not be forgotten.

King David wrote the psalm for the Israelite congregation worship service in their tabernacle (tent) before Solomon built the temple. The singers or readers of this psalm would not be new to faith in God or to his written Word. They had the books of Moses that included the CMA and should have recognized the benefits of God's relationship to mankind introduced into this world when it was created and made. Mankind should have been able to acknowledge the benefits.

Divine Action 1: Creating the Raw Materials from Nothing

In verse 19 the words, "established His throne in the heavens" is an indirect reference or allusion to God's initial divine act of creating the heavens and earth. Before that act, the heavens did not exist, and after that, his throne had been established in them. However, there is certainly no physical throne in the heavens but a spiritual one as described in 1 Kings 22:19. Rather, this language is simply asserting that he rules over everything in both heavens (angelic and physical) because he created and made it all. In summary, this verse states that God's rule extends over the entire universe he created and made at the beginning.

David used the following verses (20–22) to strongly urge everything in God's kingdom to praise their creator. Everything that was created is included in these verses by the use of the words *hosts* and *works*. These are the same words used in Genesis 2:1–2 where the products are reported at the completion of all of God's creating-and-making activity. The hosts in the heavens include both spiritual (i.e. the "angels") and physical hosts (i.e. sun, moon, and stars). They all serve God and obey his commands. The works of God are all the products of his creating and making located everywhere in the physical universe, including on Earth. A more detailed list of these same products is provided in Psalm 148.

Colossians 1:16

For by Him [Jesus Christ] all things were created, both in the heavens and on earth, visible and invisible, whether thrones or dominions or rulers or authorities—all things have been created through Him and for Him.
—Col. 1:16

This passage identifies Jesus as the Creator God. He was active during the period of creating and making of the heavens and Earth and everything in them. The "visible and invisible" refer to the tangible and intangible things that he created and made. The intangibles included thrones and dominions on Earth that God delegated to mankind from his throne and kingdom mentioned in Psalm 103:19 above. They resulted after God transferred dominion and authority over all the animals and dry land to mankind as his representative on Earth (Gen. 1:26).

John 1:1–3

In the beginning was the Word, and the Word was with God, and the Word was God. He was in the beginning with God. All things came into being through Him, and apart from Him nothing came into being that has come into being.

—John 1:1–3

These verses also identify Jesus as the Word and Creator God. Through him everything was brought into existence that ever has existed in this universe.

SCIENTIFIC TERMINOLOGY

Three Dimensional Space

Scientific observations have shown that the universe has only three spatial dimensions (3-D), although most scientists expect to find more based on some of their evolutionary theories. Everything that is made of atomic matter is three-dimensional, which means it has height, width, and depth. Three-dimensional also means that we can only move in six mutually exclusive directions—forward or backward, right or left, and up or down, as shown in Illustration 2.1.

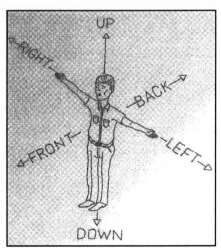

ILLUSTRATION 2.1: Possible directions of movement in 3-D space.

Divine Action 1: Creating the Raw Materials from Nothing

Because space has these dimensions, scientists have set up systems to measure distances in it. For example, the measuring system used by most scientists today has a distance unit called the light-year (ly). A light-year is the distance light can travel at its presently measured speed in one year. This distance is approximately 10 trillion kilometers (6,000 billion miles).

Big Bang Model

Scientists who support evolution have estimated that the distance to the edge of the detectable universe from the Earth in every direction is more than 13 billion light-years. This distance is beyond any distance ever measured, even to the furthest galaxies that have been detected. Even the largest and best telescopes on Earth or in orbit have not detected an edge or boundary to the universe. These scientists call the model based on this estimated distance the Big Bang or Standard Model.

This model includes many assumptions, and the theory on which it was built has not been proven. One major assumption of this theory is that an astronomical light source can be detected only as far away as its light could have traveled (at its currently measured speed locally) to reach Earth in the time since the Big Bang. The overall Big Bang theory actually depends on the universe being infinite in size, but only a small portion of it will ever be detectable by mankind. Theoretically it does not have a detectable center or edge.

The Big Bang cosmology model is presently the scientific standard explanation for the existence of everything in the universe and is promoted by the majority of cosmologists today. In this book some scientific terminology and concepts from the Big Bang model are used, but they are interpreted from a creationist perspective. We do not discuss the Big Bang model itself in any detail in this book. For a detailed description of the Big Bang model and its weaknesses from a creationist viewpoint, see Williams and Hartnett's book.[1]

Time

We infer from verse 5 of the CMA that God's basic time-measuring standard is the day. A day consisted of a period of darkness followed by a period of daylight. He established this standard on the first day, and it was established for as long as this creation remains. By definition, a creation cosmology follows the CMA in positing a standard approximately 24-hour day from the beginning of time. It is the same length of time determined by scientific methods that measure the time of one rotation of Earth as first defined by God after the sun began to shine on the fourth day (Gen. 1:16).

In scientific terms, time is measured by something moving. All movements have been found to continually proceed in a direction that advances time. Simply put, a change due to a cause results in an effect. Mankind have not found any physical means to make time go backwards, stop, or skip ahead. Our modern concept of time is shown in Illustration 2.2 by the change in time on the two clocks. According to the CMA, time started in the evening at approximately 6 PM on the first day and has been continuous ever since. Constant advance in time is shown by the clockwise arrow on the second clock.

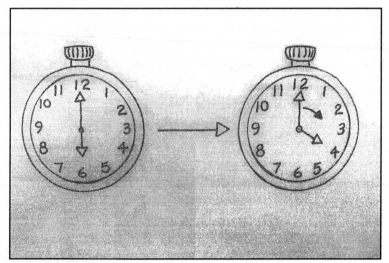

ILLUSTRATION 2.2: Time began at 6 PM on the first day and always moves clockwise.

Relativity

Albert Einstein published his famous article on the special theory of relativity in 1905. In this journal article, Einstein first theoretically established that a link exists between time and the three spatial dimensions. He assumed that link was a constant speed of light that is independent of the velocity of its source or any detection device. But he also assumed that the light was traveling at this velocity in empty space. When atomic matter is present in space, the theory was modified from special to general relativity. The resulting theory based on these conditions and assumptions has been developed to explain all the observed natural processes in the universe that change with time.

Because of Einstein's article, scientists started thinking of the physical universe as a four-dimensional (4-D) space-time continuum with three spatial dimensions and one dimension of time. Every physical process that has been discovered and measured has demonstrated that a linkage of time to space exists. For a general review of the theory of special and general relativity see any college-level modern physics text, such as Leighton's *Principles of Modern Physics.*[2]

EMR

Electromagnetic radiation (EMR) got its name from the combination of the words for electricity and magnetism. Both electricity and magnetism result from the motion of electrical charges. Negatively charged particles called electrons are constantly in motion around a positively charged nucleus in all atoms. The nucleus of an atom is made of positively charged protons and uncharged neutrons. When electrons accelerate or decelerate, they respectively absorb or emit EMR in the form of photons. The force that pulls particles of opposite charge together is called the electromagnetic force, and it is one of the four fundamental forces found in nature. The force carriers for the electromagnetic force are called photons. Photons are light quanta, the smallest parcels of electromagnetic energy that has been measured.

Darkness

Total darkness can be described scientifically as the absence of light or, more generally, of all EMR. Most people think of light as only the portion of the EMR spectrum that is visible to the human eye. The visible spectrum consists of all the colors contained in a rainbow. The colors are the individual wavelengths or frequencies that make up the sunlight humans see. The different frequencies are shown in Illustration 2.3 where a prism separates a white beam of light into colors that range from red to violet.

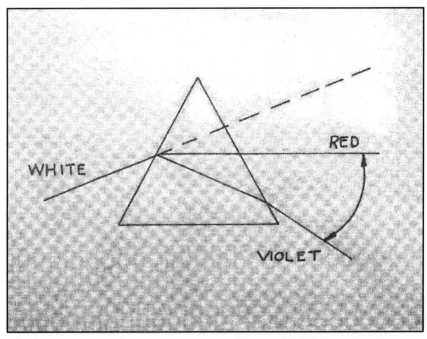

ILLUSTRATION 2.3: Prism separating the colors in visible white light.

However, the EMR spectrum continues beyond both the red and violet frequencies. Beyond the red frequency it continues into the infrared, microwave, and radio wave frequencies. On the violet end of the visible spectrum it continues into the ultraviolet, x-ray, and gamma ray frequencies. The majority of frequencies in the EMR spectrum are invisible to mankind. This means that EMR could be present but the world would still be dark to human eyes if the EMR does not contain enough energy in visible frequencies.

Atomic Matter

Material substances that are recognized by everyone consist of atoms and can be collectively called atomic matter. Atoms are the fundamental building blocks of all physical matter. The different types of atoms form the chemical elements found in nature. The chemical elements differ by the number of protons their atoms have in the nucleus. The number of electrons in the cloud around the nucleus in a neutral atom is equal to the number of protons. Atoms also form all the molecules when they share some electrons with other atoms. All the subatomic particles such as electrons, protons, and neutrons are made of a more fundamental type of material substance that provides these particles with both their mass and electric charge.

THE CM-MODEL

Divine Act 1

"In the beginning God created the heavens and the earth. At that time the earth was formless and void of life. There was darkness over the surface of the very deep earthen substance. And the Spirit of God moved over the surface of this watery substance" (Gen. 1:1–2, paraphrased).

The building of the CM-model starts with some speculation on the products of the original divine action. It begins at time zero with a primordial 4-D space-time continuum and a watery blob of an unknown substance located somewhere within it. The blob is assumed to be located at or near the center of the spatial dimensions to simplify the model. The whole 4-D space-time is totally dark because God had not yet formed light (or EMR).

Primordial Heavens

The author of the CMA reported very little about the heavens until the second day (vv. 6–8). From what is reported in Genesis 1:1–2, they were the places that contained everything that was created. They contained the primordial earth but nothing else that was tangible. It was also totally dark, and the Spirit of God was moving or hovering in it above the surface of the primordial earth. Psalm 103:19 reported that God established the throne of his kingdom in one of the heavens, in the place where the angels reside.

Total Darkness in the Universe

It is reasonable to infer from the CMA (vv. 2–3, v. 5) that God created the universe in total darkness without any EMR. He made the full spectrum of EMR, including the first daylight, in the morning as reported in verses 3–5 of the CMA. In Isaiah 45:7, God informed mankind that he forms the light and creates darkness. A totally dark place in the universe today is very difficult to find because electromagnetic forces hold all atoms together, and they radiate EMR. Scientists have found that atoms continually radiate and absorb electromagnetic radiation at any temperature above absolute zero, mainly as invisible thermal and radio-wave radiation at room temperature. At absolute zero atoms cease to exist because electrons lose their energy and fall into the nucleus of their atoms. Led by this line of reasoning, we conclude that the universe described as dark at the beginning of creation week didn't contain recognizable atomic matter or energy in the form of photons.

Primordial Earth

The CMA has listed (v. 2) several characteristics of the primordial earth. These characteristics were formlessness (no identifiable shape or internal structure) and unfilled (void of moving particles or organisms). In Genesis 1:21 the author equates living creatures to movers in the sea. In its condition at the beginning, the earth would be uninhabitable. From the two following adjectival clauses, we can add: a) it had a surface that did not emit EMR (total darkness over it), b) it was very deep (like an abyss), and c) it was made of a fluid substance (not ordinary water). These characteristics, plus our reasonable speculation, provided a scientific starting point to determine what this unknown substance was. It also leads to an estimation of the minimum amount of this universal substance that God created.

As described, the fluid could not have contained separated particles with charge and mass that were in motion, such as electrons in atoms. If charged particles were in motion, they would have emitted EMR at some frequency, and there would not have been total darkness. If particles with mass were present and in motion, the force of gravity would have pulled them together, and the blob of fluid would have imploded. An implosion is the result of gravity of an object due to its size overcoming the electromagnetic forces that hold its subatomic particles apart in atoms and molecules.

Matter and Energy Relationship

If atoms and photons did not exist immediately after the miracle, we speculate that electrons, protons, and neutrons had not yet been formed and set in motion to form atoms. The assumption that explains this is that all the material and energy used to form these subatomic particles and photons was contained in the universal fluid called earth. According to the CMA timeline, everything physically detectable in the universe was made from this universal fluid in the following four days. It would have been a perfect fluid: a fluid with no moving particles of charge or mass within it so that it did not radiate EMR or respond to gravity.

This assumption is also supported by scientific evidence. Scientists have found energy to be interchangeable with subatomic particles according to Einstein's famous relationship between energy and mass of matter ($E = Mc^2$). Energy and matter (mass) form what can be called a conversion pair where one can be converted into the other. We speculate that *the primordial fluid could be the common source of both matter and energy* formed in later divine acts. The fact that God described the blob of primordial fluid as unformed and unfilled reinforces the conclusion that atoms did not yet exist. Science has found that atoms form the basis for all physical structure and life (motion) in this universe.

Estimate of the Size of Primordial Earth

For the CM-model, this speculation concerning the perfect fluid being transformed into quanta of energy (photons) and atomic matter can be used to calculate a minimum volume of fluid that God created. This is done by estimating the size and quantity of all the known subatomic particles. Protons are one of the largest in size and longest-lived (i.e. most stable) subatomic particles. They are also one of the most numerous known to science. Because the proton is the largest and most numerous, the proton's size and quantity can be used to calculate a minimum volume for the original blob of earthen material. It would be a minimum volume because it wouldn't contain the masses of all the other subatomic particles or the equivalent mass of the energy found in all the force fields in the universe.

The radius of a proton is very small. It is approximately 10^{-15} meters (this number is a decimal point followed by fourteen zeros and a one) or smaller than one inch divided into 25,000 billion equal parts. By best estimates there are at least 10^{80} protons (Eddington's number) in the universe. This number is a one followed by 80 zeros and is so large that it is impossible to verify or even comprehend. This estimate is based on some of the assumptions underlying the Big Bang model and should never be considered a true value. Calculations using these numbers show that if the original blob had been a sphere of fluid that contained all the protons, it would have had a radius that reached from Earth to the sun. That distance is 155 million kilometers (93 million miles) and definitely meets the criteria of something that is "deep like an abyss."

It must be emphasized here that this is an estimate based on evolutionary assumptions and would only be close to the minimum amount of fluid required to make all the known atomic matter in the universe. As stated above, it doesn't include the equivalent mass of matter that would be needed if all the energy content of existing force fields in the universe was converted to matter (mass) using Einstein's relationship. Addition of the matter from this converted energy would increase by many times the minimum radius that was calculated above. What is important to remember is that even with the addition of the fluid converted to all the energy (photons) in the universe, the estimate for the radius of the blob would still be measurable and would be finite.

SCIENTIFIC EVIDENCE SUPPORTING THE CM-MODEL

Quark Soup

Recent reports on developments in high-energy physics indicate the existence of an almost perfect fluid at the subatomic level. In experiments using nucleus collisions between two gold atoms, physicists have found that the resulting product acts like it is a liquid. In simple terms, when protons and neutrons collide with enough velocity, they form a fluid-like substance that splatters initially but in a very short time reforms into protons and neutrons again. The fluid-like substance formed has been named "quark soup" and is theoretically made up of quarks and gluons.

In the Standard Model of particle physics, quarks are the next level of elementary particles that join to form protons and neutrons. Three quarks are reportedly found inside both a proton and a neutron. Gluons are the energy packets that theoretically carry the force that holds the three quarks together inside each proton or neutron. The proton has 2 "up" and 1 "down" quarks and the neutron 2 "down" and 1 "up" quarks as shown in Illustration 2.4. The forces transmitted by the gluons are the strong and weak nuclear forces that don't extend far beyond the nuclear particles.

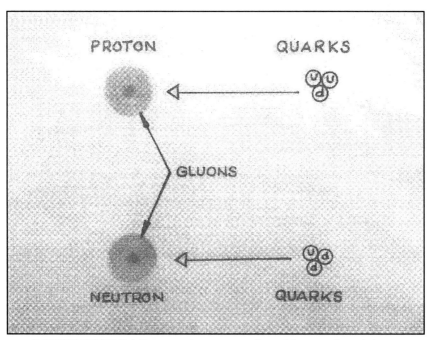

ILLUSTRATION 2.4: Protons and neutrons are formed from quarks and gluons.

The quark soup formed by the collision of nuclei was described as a nearly perfect fluid by experimenters at the Relativistic Heavy Ion Collider (RHIC) located in Brookhaven National Laboratory. It doesn't act like separated quark and gluon particles but flows like a liquid with the particles acting together like fish in a school. To a scientist this means the substance has very low viscosity. Viscosity is the collective quality of a liquid that measures how easy it is to pour. For example, water has a lower viscosity than honey at room temperature: it pours easier. A perfect fluid would have no viscosity. So the quark soup is close to a perfect fluid but still retains a very small viscosity. The properties of quark soup have only been measured at high temperatures and not at absolute zero or even at room temperature. No one has measured its temperature when it is in the form of a proton or neutron.

Because of this fluid-like collective behavior of quark soup, scientists have not been successful in efforts to obtain measurements of the characteristics of a single quark or gluon. One scientist working on the RHIC experiments stated in a *Scientific American* article:

> The protons and neutrons that form the nuclei of every atom today are relic droplets of that primordial sea, tiny subatomic prison cells in which quarks thrash back and forth, chained forever. Even in violent collisions, when the quarks seem on the verge of breaking out, new "walls" form to keep them confined. Although many physicists have tried, no one has ever witnessed a solitary quark drifting alone through a particle detector.[3]

It is obvious from this statement that it will take many more experiments with such collisions for the scientists to learn what quarks and gluons are made of and why they act collectively like a fluid.

Neutron Stars

In theory, some quark soup may exist naturally in the universe today within neutron stars. Neutron stars were regular stars at least eight times larger than the sun before they suffered an end-of-life implosion called a supernova. Supposedly, these stars are made of only neutrons formed by combining electrons with protons from atoms when the star collapsed into its new form due to gravity. Scientists have calculated the volume and mass of neutron stars from observations of these stars in a system where the neutron star and a regular star orbit each other. The internal density of neutron stars is approximately the same density as that calculated above for the original blob of fluid if it were made only of protons.[4] A teaspoon full would weigh more than a mountain on Earth. So it is possible that within a neutron star some portion of its structure may have a temperature and pressure where the neutrons have fused to form quark soup.

Black Holes

If any of the original universal fluid that was created in the beginning still exists, it would be within a black hole. It could not be detected because the event horizon of a black hole is the point beyond which nothing inside is observable. With the lack of observational data, what is inside a black hole can only be estimated from the theoretical conditions that exist inside the event horizon. We speculate that all the products formed from the universal fluid could be present within a black hole. This would include quantities of all the subatomic particles and all the energy of the force fields such as electromagnetic, gravity, and the nuclear forces. Some scientists have speculated on what a black hole could contain to explain its existence. Some of these theories involve a perfect fluid; see for example Kovtun, Son, and Starinets.[5] Humphreys gave an alternative creationist description of a black hole and its possible contents in his book *Starlight and Time*.[6]

SUMMARY

In the first divine action, God created the raw materials that he used to make the whole physical universe in the next six days. Like a design by a good architect, God's plan included the location and the building materials for constructing this habitat for humanity. Based on reasonable speculation, the CM-model described the location as a 4-D space-time continuum and the material as a relatively small volume compared to the size of the universe, but still very deep, of a perfect fluid. God also created this space-time continuum and perfect fluid in total darkness. We interpreted total darkness as a total absence of EMR of any frequency including both the visible and invisible electromagnetic spectrum, because light did not exist before the morning of the first day. Without EMR, atoms also could not have existed.

From scientific reports on quark soup, we speculate that it is the closest substance to the perfect fluid that is known and remains observable by mankind. It is theoretically possible quark soup can be found in neutron stars. But quark soup is still not the universal substance, since it does not contain the energy contained in free photons and all the force fields in the universe. The only possible place that contains all the products formed from the perfect fluid would be inside a black hole. But if the perfect fluid exists there, it is hidden from observation by the black hole event horizon.

We inferred from verse 5 of the CMA that the original period of darkness was the nighttime period of the first standard day. Later, on the fourth day, God related the standard day to the rotation rate of Earth on its axis in the light of the sun, thus the night lasted approximately twelve hours. With the physical location and raw materials created by this first miracle, the universe awaited God's following divine actions of forming and filling it.

CHAPTER 3

Divine Action 2: Calling Light into Existence

DAY 1B: MORNING HAS BROKEN

THE PREVIOUS CHAPTER described how, in beginning his work, God created the raw materials that he used to first construct a habitat for his living creatures and then to form the bodies of the creatures themselves. The raw materials that he brought into existence from nothing were the primordial heavens and earth. The CM-model represented this original universe immediately after creation as a single blob of a perfect fluid located in a 4-D space-time continuum. The blob of perfect fluid represented all the substance needed from which to make all the energy and atomic matter that has ever existed. It was formless without structure, void of motion or life, millions of kilometers deep, and totally dark without electromagnetic radiation (EMR) at any frequency.

God's second miracle then formed from these raw materials the basic building blocks and mortar for the physical universe. The author of the CMA reported in verse 3 that God called into existence a physical quantity commonly known as light. Light, or in general scientific terms electromagnetic radiation (EMR), consisted of many frequencies, both visible and invisible. Light also can be considered a member of a conversion pair with subatomic particles: one can be converted into the other. Therefore, we speculate that when God first formed light, he also formed subatomic particles. We infer from verse 5 of the CMA that this miracle took place at dawn of the first day and actually caused that dawn.

Where the light came from has been and still is a subject of debate among creation scientists. How God provided the daylight for days one through three without the existence of the light providers—the sun and all the other stars—was not answered in the CMA. In Isaiah 45:7 God stated that he forms light and creates darkness. This verse implies he did not create light from nothing but formed it from the universal substance primordial earth. The CM-model is based on reasonable speculation that the sources for visible light on all of the first three days are natural processes that existed after God formed light. These natural processes existed once light and subatomic particles were formed as a conversion pair, because God pronounced light and everything related to it complete and perfect (Gen. 1:4). On the first two days, the source of daylight had to be universe-wide, since stars and planets were only just beginning to be formed. By the third daylight period, the focus of the CMA has changed to the human habitat on the planet known as Earth, so since that time, only the light on Earth has defined the standard day.

The relationship between light and atomic matter was one of the most fundamental ever discovered by scientists about the nature of the universe. In simple terms, this relationship implied that atoms (matter) and light (energy) as a conversion pair had a common source. Logically, this relationship leads to the conclusion that without light, the atoms cannot exist, and without atoms, the universe would be dark. The atoms formed the basic building blocks, while light, as the conveyer of the electromagnetic force, supplied some of the mortar from which the universe was constructed. The other three fundamental forces (gravity, weak and strong nuclear forces) supplied the remainder of the mortar.

Many mysteries involving the relationship between atoms and light were hidden from mankind until recent times. No doubt, more mysteries still exist about this relationship that may be uncovered in the future. One prominent remaining mystery is that light and atoms share dual characteristics of being both wave-like and particle-like.

The wave-like nature of atoms has been demonstrated by a device that produced a beam of atoms in which the atoms are all in-phase with each other. When things are in-phase, they form wave fronts like rows of soldiers marching in a military parade as shown in Illustration 3.1. The device produced the atomic equivalent of in-phase photons from a laser. Such a device has been called an "atom laser." Waves of atoms or subatomic particles are called *de Broglie waves* after the theoretical physicist who first predicted, in 1924, that electrons have an associated wavelength.

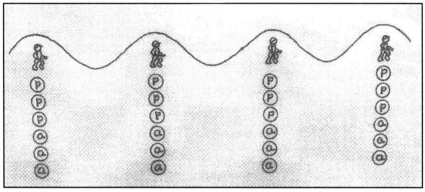

ILLUSTRATION 3.1: In-phase wave-like behavior of marching men, photons (p), and atoms (a).

OTHER BIBLICAL REFERENCES TO MIRACLE 2

Psalm 104:1b–2a

You are very great; You are clothed with splendor and majesty, covering Yourself with light as with a cloak.

—Ps. 104:1b–2a

These verses are part of the theme of a psalm or hymn that praises God for his wondrous works during creation week. Indeed, the whole psalm consists of allusions (indirect references) that are each related to a miracle during the first five days of his workweek. Also, the allusions to those miracles are in the same order they were reported in the CMA.

Like Psalm 103, this psalm was written for the Israelite congregation in Jerusalem. Verse 1 began with the same clause used at the end of Psalm 103: "Bless the LORD, O my soul!" These are the only two psalms that use this clause. This psalm continues (v. 1b) with the summary statement that God is great and clothed in splendor and majesty. In verse 2, the author alluded to two miracles God performed when he created and made the universe: covering himself in physical light and stretching out the heavens (this will be the subject of the next chapter).

In verse 2a the psalmist provided a snapshot of God forming the light on the first day as if it was a cloak that displays his splendor and majesty. This allusion to the forming of light can be best understood in context of the report given in the CMA. In Genesis 1:2c, "the Spirit of God was moving [or hovering] over the surface of the waters" and then God spoke the words, "Let there be light" (Gen. 1:3). We can infer from this scenario that the light God formed enveloped the blob and traveled into the heavens above its surface. It is also reasonable to picture the hovering Spirit wrapping himself in this newly formed light.

Isaiah 45:7

The One forming light and creating darkness, causing well-being and creating calamity; I am the LORD *who does all these.*
—Isaiah 45:7

This verse reported God saying that he is the one that forms the light. This can be applied to Genesis 1:3 where he formed light for the first time. He didn't create it at the beginning but formed it from something he had created. The Hebrew word translated *forming* is also used in Genesis 2:7 to describe God forming man from the dust of the ground.

The second clause reported that God creates darkness. This can be applied to Genesis 1:1 where he created everything in darkness, including the heavens and earth. At that time it would have been utter darkness or the total absence of light. This is reported in Genesis 1:2 as "darkness was over the surface of the deep." We infer from this that darkness was everywhere because God had not yet formed light.

The following set of parallel clauses states that God causes well-being and creates calamity. It is similar in literary structure because calamity is the opposite of well-being like darkness is the opposite of light.

Scientific Terminology

Light

Light has been characterized in scientific literature as both freely moving energy and a conveyer of the electromagnetic force. Historically, scientists have described it in two ways: as a particle of energy (photon or quantum) or as an EMR wave. In recent times, the consensus among leading scientists is that it exhibits both characteristics simultaneously.

The particle characteristics of light were discovered because a light beam transfers energy to atoms in discrete amounts. The energy in a light quantum or photon is directly proportional to its frequency. This relationship is demonstrated by higher frequency photons, like x-rays, carrying more energy than lower frequency photons, like radio waves. The two views of light can be reconciled because the smallest amount of energy that a certain frequency (or wavelength) of EMR can transfer to an atomic particle is equal to the energy carried by a photon of that frequency.

Theoretically, photons are characterized as particles that are always in motion. Photons start moving at a constant speed when they are emitted by electrons and end their journey at the same speed when they are absorbed. In a vacuum on Earth's surface, the speed of photons has been measured at nearly 300,000 kilometers per second (greater than 186,000 miles per second).

Atomic Matter

Scientists have found that atoms are the basic building blocks of all the matter that has been detected in the universe. In turn, atoms are made of three long-lived subatomic particles: protons, neutrons, and electrons. Most other subatomic particles are difficult to detect and many are short-lived. The only way to detect most of these other particles is by their interaction with the three main particles in atomic matter.

Even individual atoms lose electrons, protons, and neutrons, which can change them into an ion or even a different chemical element over a period of time. Chemical elements are a single type of atom and are either a gas, liquid, or solid at room temperature and pressure. Chemical elements are identified by the number of protons they have in their nucleus. That number is called the atomic number of the element. There are 83 chemical elements that have a stable nucleus and exist in nature for relatively long periods of time. The other 25–30 elements are radioactive and decay into other elements in a short period of time.

The number of electrons in a neutral atom is also equal to the atomic number. Scientists envision electrons existing in orbital shells around the nucleus. When atoms lose one or more of their atomic number of electrons to other atoms, they become positive ions. If atoms gain extra electrons, they become negative ions. Positive and negative ions usually join with each other by chemical bonds to form molecules and chemical compounds. Illustration 3.2 shows the particle composition of a water molecule.

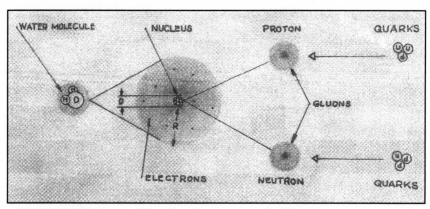

ILLUSTRATION 3.2: Particle composition of molecular water. D represents the diameter of the nucleus, and R represents the radius of the atom.

Scientists have observed that the composition of atomic matter in the form of chemical elements, molecules, and compounds is the same everywhere in the observable universe. The majority of atomic matter in the universe is in the form of molecules. Chemical compounds can contain many different elements in their molecules. Atoms are considered the basic building blocks of all matter in the universe. They are also the continual source of light that lights the world.

Motion

Many physical concepts in the CM-model involve motion. The simple definition of motion is a change of position in 3-D space with time. More generally, any change with time can be called motion. We speculate that God started all motion when he formed light. Some reasons for this are that, before the miracle that brought light into existence, only the Spirit was moving in the universe (v. 2); light itself does not exist in its present form unless it is in motion; and energy in the form of photons is required to put other particles into motion. All motion is relative to a starting point from which a change can be measured. Spatial motions are measured in a fixed coordinate system centered on a point of reference. This system is called a reference frame, and it provides a way to measure the distance and the direction traveled by the object. Time, as the fourth dimension, is required to measure how fast the change took place.

Motion is considered a 4-D process because it involves both 3-D space and time. When the molecules composing air are moving, the result of their motion as a group is called wind. Its rate of motion is measured as air speed. Electromagnetic and gravitational forces are the known causes of wind. In Amos 4:13 the author reported that God creates the wind. We infer from this verse that God created the forces that cause the air molecules to move in a group.

The concept of motion can be generalized to include any change caused by a natural process. Physical process rates are measured by a change in some parameter with respect to time. Some familiar measures of atomic or molecular motion that are present in all matter are temperature and viscosity, as mentioned in the previous chapter.

As an example of motion in a nuclear process, alpha decay is measured by a change from one atomic element to another. The number of atoms of a radioactive element in a large group that change into another element in a certain length of time is called the decay rate of that radioactive element. This process takes place when the nucleus of a radioactive atom emits an alpha particle (the nucleus of a helium atom). The decay of uranium into lead is a well-known example that occurs in nature. Many other examples of physical processes that have rates of change are found in the physical sciences, such as geology, chemistry, and biology. Some of these will be described in following chapters.

Force Fields

Scientists have shown through quantum mechanics theory and experiments that the exchange of energy quanta (photons) between electrons and the nucleus of an atom establishes the force field within the atom. The force is directed between the negatively charged orbiting electron and the positively charged protons of the nucleus. This force field holds the electrons in their orbital shells around the nucleus. It is similar to planets that are held in orbits around the sun by the force of gravity. In the atom, the force itself is called the electromagnetic force and is one of the four forces that scientists have identified. The other three forces are the strong and weak nuclear forces and the force of gravity.

A weak nuclear force field is located within both the protons and neutrons that form the nucleus of atoms. It is the force that holds them together as distinct particles. Theoretically, this force field is formed by the exchange of gluons between the three quarks within each particle. Both quarks and gluons were mentioned in the previous chapter as components of quark soup.

The strong nuclear force holds the protons and neutrons to each other to form the nucleus of an atom. Two protons normally would repel each other because of the electromagnetic force between two positive charges. The strong nuclear force is stronger than the electromagnetic force at short range and holds two protons next to each other. This force field is also formed by exchange of gluons but between quarks in one particle and quarks in the other. The energy that the strong nuclear force field contains is called the binding energy of the nucleus. This is the source of the energy that is given off as radiation (the whole EMR spectrum) when nuclei of atoms are split in nuclear fission or fused in nuclear fusion. The great strength of this nuclear force is demonstrated in the large amounts of energy released in nuclear bomb explosions.

Gravity is the force that governs the position and motion of large objects made of atomic matter relative to each other in space and time. How this force field is formed has not been discovered at this time. Many theories have been proposed, but so far none have explained the source of gravity and exactly how it works. What scientists have determined is that the force of gravity is related to the mass of atomic matter, and it is always an attractive force drawing two objects together. It is also known that two objects will attract each other with greater force as they approach one another. Mass is another term used for an object's weight. Weight is the mass of an object measured on Earth where the gravitational force is well known. Mass is used by scientists instead of weight because it can be applied to measurements of any object, even those that cannot be measured on Earth. This is much more useful in places like on the moon, on other planets, or anywhere in outer space.

The forces and the force fields used to describe them can be considered the mortar that holds the universe together. The electromagnetic force holds atoms together and also connects them to each other in gases, liquids, and solid compounds. Atoms and their subatomic particles are the building blocks, while light or EMR was the mortar that formed the basic structure of all atomic matter that has been discovered by mankind. As shown in Illustration 3.3, the electromagnetic force can either repel or attract. The other three are only attractive forces.

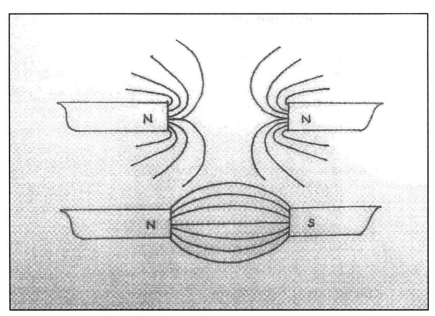

ILLUSTRATION 3.3: Electromagnetic force fields between two magnets. Top shows repelling and bottom shows attracting magnets.

Black Holes

Scientists have detected spherical volumes in space that do not emit any EMR. However, these spherical volumes interact with stars and other atomic matter near them through the force of gravity. Scientists have called these invisible spheres black holes. Their boundaries have been detected using non-visible radiation such as x-ray and radio waves. This invisible EMR is caused by atomic matter being torn apart by gravity as it approaches the boundary of the black hole, which is called the event horizon.

Theoretically, a black hole is a spherically shaped volume containing enough condensed atomic matter that its gravity is so strong it keeps all EMR within its boundary. Any EMR or atomic matter that enters this boundary just disappears. Scientists have measured the amount of gravity associated with a black hole by the effects it has on adjacent objects such as stars or molecular clouds. From that, they can compute the amount of mass the black hole represents. With that value they can calculate the size of its event horizon. This size closely fits the observations of where the x-rays and radio waves originate outside the event horizon of black holes they have measured.

Astronomers explain the existence of small black holes as remnants formed when giant stars implode in what are called supernova. They have calculated, using computer simulations, the mass a supernova product should have and then determined its event horizon radius. Black holes of this relative size have been found in binary star systems that have both a normal star and an invisible mass. The size and weight of these black holes have verified the calculations and theory. These same astronomers, however, have not found a simple explanation for the super-massive black holes found at the center of galaxies. These very large black holes will be discussed in more detail in the next chapter.

THE CM-MODEL

The CM-model described the universe before dawn of the first day as a 4-D space-time continuum that contained a relatively small indistinct blob of the universal substance a perfect fluid. If it had been a sphere, the blob would have had an estimated minimum radius that reached from the orbit of Earth to the sun, which made it extremely deep. We have speculated that the blob contained no internal structure or moving parts (subatomic particles). Because particles and motion are required for temperature and viscosity, the blob would have been at zero absolute temperature and did not have any viscosity. In this chapter, we extend the CM-model to describe some of possible changes to this blob resulting from the second divine act. We make additions to the model that explain the conditions that appear to have been present as reported in verse 5 of the CMA just prior to the beginning of the second day.

Divine Act 2

> *Then God said, "Let there be light"; and there was light. God saw that the light was good; and God separated the light from the darkness.*
> —Gen. 1:3–4

By a miracle, God formed light, or more generally EMR, from the raw material he had created. We speculate that the light was formed from the perfect fluid of the primordial earth blob. Simultaneous with the forming of EMR, subatomic particles such as quarks, gluons, and electrons, were also formed from the fluid. We assume that this divine action changed the whole primordial universe, where portions of the fluid within the blob were transformed into photons and moving particles, and the light also moved into the heavens surrounding the blob.

The lack of scientific knowledge in three basic areas of particle physics makes it difficult to model the transformation of the perfect fluid into light and atomic matter. Scientists have not discovered: a) the source of charge on electrons and protons, b) the source of mass of the subatomic particles, and c) what makes quark soup act collectively as a fluid. The charged particles were the source of the electromagnetic force, and the mass of the particles was related somehow to the force of gravity. The fluid-like properties of quark soup were related to the strong and weak nuclear forces. In summary, scientists have not been able to explain why any of the four forces exist. For the CM-model, it is enough to know that God created these forces in their final form when he formed light and the subatomic particles. And according to the CMA, they became apparent as products of his second divine act.

Light and Atom Formation

We assume that when God formed light, he made the whole spectrum of EMR with the same miracle. Every frequency of light has the same physical characteristics. Therefore, the original light included everything from the highest frequency gamma rays to the lowest frequency radio waves. Mankind have detected neither end of the EMR spectrum of frequencies. Scientists are limited in detecting the ends of the EMR spectrum by the lack of suitable materials sensitive to these extremely high or low frequencies.

We speculate that the transformation within the blob of fluid took place rapidly. There is no reason to believe that the morning and daylight portion of the first day were longer than any other day since. As described in chapter 1, this miracle most likely was a supernaturally accelerated process that took place in the 4-D space-time continuum that God had created in the beginning.

As some of the perfect fluid in the blob was transformed into light and subatomic particles, the original blob as a whole would have begun to change in volume, density, temperature, and viscosity. This had to happen to accommodate the resulting products (initially quark soup and electrons). For the model, the photons that are always moving transferred some of their kinetic energy to the subatomic particles by collisions so that they accelerated to high speeds. One requirement for particles in motion was room within the blob material so that they could move. This space within the blob could only be provided if its overall volume grew in size by expanding.

As the volume of the blob increased, the density of the particles it contained constantly changed. As more and more particles were formed, and the motion of subatomic particles increased, the temperature of the whole blob also would have started to rise above absolute zero. The quark soup that formed first and later turned into protons and neutrons would have had the small viscosity attributed to it as a high-temperature fluid.

Plasma Formation

The three basic subatomic particles that formed all atoms are electrons, protons, and neutrons. We speculate that the nuclei of atoms would have formed first from the quark soup and then captured free electrons to form atoms. The simplest atom, hydrogen, has a single proton in its nucleus. When electrons and protons collided, they would have formed neutrons. Higher-atomic-number nuclei would have formed by fusing hydrogen nuclei with additional protons and neutrons.

The original nuclei that formed could not have captured electrons immediately. The particles were moving about too rapidly. Therefore, they remained in the form of ions for at least a short period of time. During that time, large groups of freely moving ions would have formed a gaseous fluid called plasma. Since the distances involved were subatomic in these early transformations, the time it took would have been relatively short, similar to nuclear bomb explosions. In the Big Bang model, this phase of development took place in less than six minutes. But since the CM-model started under entirely different conditions (transformed from a perfect fluid) and models a miracle, the time cannot be determined any closer than a half day (twelve hours).

Only after the plasma cooled by expanding could atoms of hydrogen or other elements begin forming as the ions captured electrons from the plasma. The blob must have grown tremendously in volume to make room for hydrogen and larger atoms. A short time later the atoms were also moving about in a gaseous mixture with the plasma. A hydrogen atom with its electron required 100,000 times the volume of the proton in its nucleus. And there is no way to know how much space was between these atoms at that time.

We speculate for the CM-model that the fluid-like blob developed quickly into a mixture of high-temperature plasma, atoms of lower atomic number, and some remaining original fluid once the transformations had progressed. The plasma could have appeared originally in lightning-like streams that emitted light much brighter than the surface of the sun. These streams of plasma would have formed volumes of atomic matter in their paths. They would have been interspersed with volumes of untransformed perfect fluid. The blob's overall volume would have continued to grow as more and more of the perfect fluid was transformed into EMR and atomic matter.

Light Separated from Darkness

The author of the CMA reported in verse 4 that the light was good in God's eyes. That implied it was perfect and complete. We infer that the miracle that formed light also established its relationships to atomic matter, since they were formed as a conversion pair.

In the same verse we read, "God separated the light from the darkness." The Hebrew word that is translated *separated* actually describes two actions. The first action was division of one item into two or more, and the second action was placing something between the items as a barrier against the items getting back together. In simple terms, God established some laws of nature that resulted in places where light was intense and other places where there was little (or at least less) light that could be called darkness. The author of the CMA did not reveal how God did this. After light formed, it was free to travel where total darkness had been created in the universe. To model the universe after God separated light from darkness, a new definition for darkness seems to be required. The following physical concepts are possible options that fit the CMA description of darkness following verse 4 and take into account its new relationship to light and atomic matter.

Concept 1

On the first day there was only a single blob of primordial earth. For the model, this blob must have contained both light and dark areas after the separation of light and darkness by the end of the day. Light that left the blob would continue into space, replacing the absence of light (or darkness) that God originally created there. A simple explanation for the separation of light from darkness could be the separation of light from its original source: the perfect fluid that had been totally dark. This took place when light and atomic matter formed and God's separation made it permanent. In other words, once light and atomic matter form, they will never recombine on their own to form a dark perfect fluid.

Concept 2

Mankind, when created, could see with their eyes only the small portion of the EMR spectrum that is called visible light. Without modern technology and its instrumentation, the remainder of the EMR spectrum remained invisible or dark. Most of the invisible EMR frequencies have been continuously present almost everywhere in the universe since the morning of the first day. Therefore, separation of light from darkness, if applied to mankind, could be described as the absence of visible light in some places in the universe, while other places contained visible light.

One possible cause of light and dark areas in the blob is suggested by the concept of night as defined in verse 5 of the CMA. God defined night as the dark portion of the day but, as is commonly known, nights after the fourth day contained some visible light from the moon and stars. The cause of darkness at night on Earth is the planet forming a shadow in the light from the sun and shielding half its sphere from the sunlight. Nighttime is defined as darkness in a shadow where a lesser amount of light is visible than within the direct light of the sun. Darker and lighter places could have existed within the blob of fluid-like matter. The blob contained both some perfect fluid that was totally dark and high temperature plasma that gave off intense light. This combination could have formed shadows behind remaining pockets of the dark original fluid.

Concept 3

Another possible cause for the separated light and dark areas in the blob could have resulted from volumes within the blob absorbing light but not emitting any. Such volumes as described earlier are called black holes. The force of gravity that forms a black hole could certainly have been activated at the formation of atomic matter. As black holes formed, they would keep any light within their event horizon and appear dark because they only absorbed light. The force of gravity could have built up as the atoms formed until it reached a level strong enough to pull atoms together into clumps. These clumps could have formed event horizons within the expanding fluid blob when their mass reached the threshold level for forming black holes.

Since the blob was extremely deep, we speculate that the blob didn't expand uniformly. This uneven expansion would cause some areas in the blob where atomic particles were held in clumps under extreme pressures right after they formed. If enough particles were confined in a small enough volume, the gravitational field they produced could have trapped plasma and some original fluid within an event horizon.

For the purpose of the CM-model, we chose a combination of all three concepts to describe a blob in the universe compatible with the CMA at the end of the first day. For the next phase of the model in the following chapter, it is necessary that the dark areas in the blob included black holes that formed due to gravity. These black holes formed an envelope around remaining pockets of the original fluid and interspersed plasma. The significance of black holes containing some perfect fluid will become apparent in the next chapter when the model is extended to include the formation of white holes.

Both the black holes and independent remaining pockets of the perfect fluid were capable of casting shadows from areas of intense light. Also, once the light and atoms formed, no natural process has been discovered that recombines them into a perfect fluid. Theoretically, the only place in the universe this recombination could take place is within a black hole, and if it happens there, it will never be observed.

The Size of the Expanding Primordial Earth

An interim size estimate for the primordial earth blob when it had expanded for half a day after light started forming can be calculated using reasonable assumptions. The equivalent spherical volume approach used in the previous chapter is one assumption. The CM-model described a blob of many black holes formed due to God separating the light and darkness. For a minimum estimate of the number of black holes that formed, it is reasonable to assume that number was, at least, equal to the number of known galaxies in the universe. For the CM-model, we postulate in the next chapter that each ultra-massive black hole formed a galaxy on the second day. The average size of an ultra-massive black hole is calculated from the mass of all the stars and any remaining black hole in an average-sized galaxy.

This calculation was done only to provide an estimate of the expanded blob size. It does not represent what actually happened as God formed the universe. For example, the CM-model does not start with a single black hole, as the calculation would indicate. However, with reasonable speculation, the black holes within the blob were merely forming and did not reach their full size and gravitational potential until after they were supernaturally separated at the beginning of the second day. The result of the calculation is merely an interim estimate for the minimum size of the blob before it was separated to fill the universe with galaxies and their stars.

Astronomers consider the Milky Way galaxy to be an average galaxy, and it has approximately 400 billion stars. Astronomers estimate that there are approximately 170 billion galaxies in the known universe. Using these values, the minimum radius of a spherical volume containing all this matter in a single black hole would have a radius of approximately 1,000 light years. This radius is very small compared to what evolutionary scientists have determined as the radius of the present universe in their Big Bang model. Their calculated radius is nearly 14 billion light years. Even the radius of the Milky Way galaxy, which is approximately 50,000 light years, is fifty times as large as this interim estimate.

The new size estimate indicates that the blob grew a minimum of 100 million times from the original blob of perfect fluid in approximately twelve hours. According to the CMA, this expansion took no more than half the first day (daylight portion only). The great expansion indicated would have happened at a very high rate. That rate would be considered impossible based on natural processes alone.

The scientists who support the Big Bang theory have gotten past a similar problem by claiming that space itself expanded. That is a physical concept that has not actually been demonstrated to be possible, but has only been proposed as a theoretical solution to a significant problem in their model. In their theory and model, they claimed that the atoms formed in a few minutes after a very large expansion of space called inflation. However, they have determined no natural cause for the inflation nor explained how atoms could form in rapidly expanding space. In simple terms, they have not provided evidence to support their claims. Another problem with inflation that has not been solved is this: If space expanded faster than the speed of light and gravity, how was gravity able to form the stars and their galaxies during the process of the expansion?

Scientists have documented that light itself, much less atomic particles with mass, can travel only a relatively short distance (a little over 8 billion miles or one 750th of a light year) in twelve hours. In other words, if the blob expanded to a radius greater than 1,000 light years, both the light and atomic matter in it must have been traveling at much greater than the presently measured speed of light: indeed, at least 750,000 times faster (750 times the estimated 1000 ly radius). Scientists who support evolution would describe this speed as superluminal, meaning faster than the speed of light would allow. Their thinking is limited to processes that are natural, and their conclusion would be to say it is impossible. But with God nothing is impossible (Luke 1:37), and supernaturally accelerated rates could have made the event happen in the reported time.

SCIENTIFIC EVIDENCE SUPPORTING THE CM-MODEL

There are at least three bodies of scientific evidence that support the CM-model: a) the universal distribution of EMR in the universe, called the cosmic microwave background radiation (CMBR); b) the intergalactic medium (IGM) of atoms and molecules that has been detected in space between galaxies; and c) the existence of super-massive black holes at the center of spiral galaxies that are close enough to Earth to have been observed.

CMBR

Scientists looking for electromagnetic noise sources in a newly designed microwave receiver first discovered CMBR in 1965. They measured a noise source that was constant almost everywhere they pointed their receiver into the sky. Their measurements showed that an equivalent temperature of this noise source was approximately 3 Kelvins (3 degrees above absolute zero). Later experiments have refined the temperature measurement to 2.725 K.

Because the temperature was the same in almost every direction, the source had to be distributed evenly in space around Earth. Supporters of the evolutionary standard cosmology model claimed: a) the CMBR was emitted by the hot gases that resulted from the Big Bang; b) it has traveled almost 14 billion light years to reach the Earth; and c) the peak wavelength of the radiation was originally visible but has been red shifted to the microwave region due to the expansion of space during its journey since the Big Bang. For a detailed description of the role of CMBR in the evolution of the Big Bang model, see Alpher and Herman's book *Genesis of the Big Bang.*[1]

The CM-model explains the existence of the CMBR quite differently. This radiation is the remnant of the daylight of the first day modified by subsequent events during creation week. The main modification—its shift in frequency—will be discussed in detail in the next chapter along with where the sources of CMBR could have been located.

IGM

The second area of support is the universal composition of matter. All matter has the same basic atomic structure within it. Everywhere scientists looked in the universe, the atomic structure was always the same, with the protons and neutrons in a nucleus and electrons located in orbital shells around it. This basic structure required that the EMR (photons) and the subatomic particles of electrons, protons, and neutrons were present at the same time when the atoms formed. We can infer from this relationship that there was a common originating source for these basic building blocks and mortar of atomic matter. The dual particle-like and wave-like natures of both light and subatomic particles add further support to the concept of a single common source.

Clouds of hot atomic and molecular gases have been found in space even between galaxies. These gas clouds have been called intergalactic media because of their location. They are detectable because the gas is highly ionized, and ions of all atoms absorb and emit radiation at their own specific frequencies. Heavy ions as large as argon have been identified in the IGM.[2] IGM and its origins will also be discussed in detail in the next chapter.

Black Holes

A third area of scientific support is the recently documented existence of super-massive black holes at the center of all spiral galaxies near enough to Earth so that their centers can be observed. One has also been detected at the center of the Milky Way galaxy.[3] The existence of super-massive black holes in the center of galaxies supports the CM-model, because in the model, they are the remnants of ultra-massive black holes. In the next chapter, these much larger black holes are modeled as the source from which each galaxy formed by their spewing out of the material that became stars, planets, and moons.

Super-massive black holes have been detected in thousands of galaxies recently due to the orbiting of x-ray telescopes on satellites above Earth's atmosphere. (X-rays do not pass through the atmosphere, so surface-based telescopes are blind to the x-ray sources.) The detected x-rays from black holes are produced just outside their event horizon.[4] They are the result of matter being torn apart and accelerated as it approaches the black hole's boundary. Black holes could be the answer to God's inquiry of Job about where darkness resides in the universe, as recorded in Job 38:19–20.

Everywhere in the universe, atomic matter is found in clumps called galaxies with great distances between. Even scientists who support evolution acknowledge that black holes had a role in the formation of these galaxies. In an article on super-massive black holes in a nearby galaxy (M87), the authors state: "It now appears that the evolution of galaxies is intimately linked with the growth of the super-massive black holes at their centers."[5]

SUMMARY

The starting point for the CM-model was a blob of a perfect fluid-like substance that had no internal structure (i.e. particles or quanta of energy) and therefore had no viscosity or temperature. God created the blob in a 4-D space-time continuum that was totally dark; it was without light (EMR) of any kind. At God's command for light to form, photons and subatomic particles formed within the blob with both having particle-like and wave-like characteristics. For the CM-model, we speculated that these energy and subatomic particles formed along lightning-like streaks that turned rapidly into streams of hot plasma.

Photons that formed along these streaks began to travel in every direction, and some even traveled out into the space beyond the surface of the blob. Three kinds of subatomic particles (electrons, protons, and neutrons) were of primary interest for the model because they have long lives. They joined to form all the atoms or building blocks of matter in the universe, each held together internally by electromagnetic and nuclear forces. These subatomic particles had both charge and mass that caused them to stay closer to their point of origin for a longer period of time than the freed photons.

Physical laws governed the interaction between the particles of energy (photons and gluons) and all the subatomic particles. Those laws were established in the initial part of the transformation process and became part of it. They took the form of electromagnetic and nuclear forces and could be described as the mortar that holds together the basic structure of atoms.

Initially, the transfer of energy and momentum from the photons put all the newly formed particles into rapid motion so that the subatomic particles formed plasma. As the blob rapidly grew, the plasma cooled and the particles slowed down. Protons and neutrons first joined to form nuclei of atoms with low atomic number. As the cooling continued, these nuclei captured electrons and formed atoms. Once atoms formed, they joined other atoms to form molecules. As the collections of atoms and molecules grew, they acquired the physical characteristics that are known as viscosity and temperature. When the collections of atomic matter had grown into larger and larger clumps, the force of gravity built to a level where it pulled clumps of atomic matter together and condensed them into black holes.

By the end of the first day, the created primordial earth had expanded by over 100 million times its original size. It now contained both EMR and atomic matter with significant amounts of the atomic matter and untransformed perfect fluid disappearing into black holes. All the properties and natural processes related to light and atomic matter had been established for all time. This miracle produced the first offsprings of the primordial earth and their rapid maturation into the bricks and mortar of the universe.

God first completed the building blocks and the mortar that holds them together in a basic structure for the universe he designed and then continued to build with them. In scientific terms, the universe passed from a perfect fluid through an initial radiation-dominated era into the matter-dominated era that still exists today. This transition took place very rapidly in the second half of the first day.

It makes no difference if the model described the sequence of events correctly or not, the products that resulted still exist for all mankind to see. The spectacular process that took place in less than half of the first day with a single command of the Creator and Maker can only be described as miraculous. It shows he is great and clothed in splendor and majesty (Ps. 104:1).

CHAPTER 4

Divine Action 3: Separating the Waters and Making the Expanse

DAY 2: STRETCHING OUT, SPREADING OUT

EVENTS ON THE second day seem to be the least understood of all the reports given in the CMA. All well-known creation models have begun with either molecular water (H_2O) as the substance of primordial earth or a planetary Earth submerged in an excess of such water. The supporters of the latter position then postulated that God separated most of the water from the planet and stored it in the heavens above. Those who started with only molecular water haven't described in any detail how only water could result in all the other chemical elements and compounds found within Earth and all the stars, planets, and moons in the universe.

Many of the older models used the water that was separated from the planet as a water source for explaining the forty days of rain at the beginning of the great flood event recorded in Genesis 6–8. This was a major premise of what has been called the Canopy Model. A general technical review of that model can be found in a paper presented by G. S. Jorgensen at the Third International Conference on Creationism 1994.[1] Even with a source for the water, it was still difficult to explain how a canopy could exist for a long time in or near to extraterrestrial space above Earth.

Both of these model types neglected certain physical characteristics of water molecules, which make common water impossible prior to the forming of light. It is even more physically impossible if the water is located on the surface of a planet without a protective atmosphere. First, water molecules themselves never existed without light photons, or EMR, as explained in the previous chapter. Atoms and molecules of all types are held together by electromagnetic force that is transmitted by photons (EMR). Second, water would not have remained a liquid on the surface of a planet without an internal or external source of heat (thermal radiation, also EMR). Most of these models therefore had a major problem with fitting their primordial earth into a real physical universe. They had another problem in fitting it into the CMA timeline. For example, most of these modelers explained the existence of all the other heavenly bodies by a special creation event on the fourth day that is not reported in the CMA or anywhere else in the Scriptures.

In the CM-model, the term *waters* has been accepted as an adjectival noun describing the original fluid state of primordial earth, as inferred from verse 2 of the CMA. A fluid is a substance that flows, and it can be either gaseous or liquid in nature. It is used in that verse to describe the original perfect fluid material that continues to change form during the transformations induced by the miracles God used to build the universe. Not until the third day is actual molecular water reported by the CMA as existing on Earth.

Originally, this watery universal substance consisted of all the ingredients, in the form of a perfect fluid, needed to form electromagnetic energy waves or photons, force fields, and all the basic subatomic particles. With his second divine action, God changed at least some of this perfect fluid into building materials—light and atomic matter—with which he made the chemical elements that are found everywhere in the physical universe. They formed the mortar and bricks that make up everything recognized as a form of atomic matter. When God formed these materials, he also established all the physical laws that govern the relationships between them.

Following the CMA timeline, the next reported divine action was a separation of the fluids resulting from the second miracle. God took the raw materials he had made from the perfect fluid and built the physical structure of the heavens, including all the celestial spheres. We speculate that he first divided the blob of fluid containing EMR, atomic matter, and some remaining perfect fluid into billions of droplets in the form of ultra-massive black holes that would become galaxies. He then distributed the celestial bodies (that become stars, planets, moons, etc.) into a galaxy through white holes in each ultra-massive black hole event horizon. The celestial bodies were all separated from each other by nearly empty space. The structure he made was the stretched-out heavens or expanse that consisted of the galaxies of celestial bodies and the force fields that control their motions and determine their positions relative to each other.

In scientific terms, God made the geometry of space recognized by today's scientists as governed by the theory of general relativity. The results of miracle 3 can be observed in the heavens to this day. These physical heavens declared the glory of God and constituted the expanse with all its hosts that showed his handiwork for mankind, who were created on the sixth day (Ps. 19:1).

OTHER BIBLICAL REFERENCES TO MIRACLE 3

Psalm 104:2b–5

> *Stretching out heaven like a tent curtain. He lays the beams of His upper chambers in the waters; He makes the clouds His chariot; He walks upon the wings of the wind; He makes the winds His messengers, flaming fire His ministers. He established the earth upon its foundations, so that it will not totter forever and ever.*
>
> —Ps. 104:2b–5

In these verses, the author continued the theme of the whole psalm—allusions to the making of the physical universe, for which God should be praised. In verse 2b, he provided a snapshot of God stretching out the heavens as a curtain. This allusion can be found in more than ten other verses in the Bible. The author of the CMA reported this event as God commanding, "Let there be an expanse in the midst of the waters, and let it separate the waters from the waters" (Gen. 1:6). This stretching out of the heavens resulted in the separation of the fluid blob of primordial earth into all the celestial spheres found in the heavens. Then in Gen. 1:8, God named the expanse that resulted "heaven(s)."

In verses 3–5 of this psalm, the author provided snapshots with more details of God's wondrous handiwork and a display of his great power in making the stretched-out heavens and all their hosts. The context places these snapshots between the start of the stretching and when the celestial bodies (including the planet Earth) have arrived at their positions in extraterrestrial space. This was consistent with the CMA timeline. God separated the original blob, made the expanse, and formed the celestial bodies on the second day before he chose a particular planet to transform further at the start of the third day.

"He lays the beams of His upper chambers *[with]* the waters" (Ps. 104:3a, emphasis added).

The first snapshot in these verses pictures God laying the beams of his upper chambers with the waters. To paraphrase this clause, God constructed the basic structure of the physical heavens with the separated drops of fluids. Here "laying beams" pictured the building of the basic structure and "His upper chambers" represented the spiritual heavens where he set up his throne (Ps. 103:19). The physical heavens were formed as a part of the spiritual heavens. The "waters" of the second day were still fluids in transition from the perfect fluid to the final products made of atomic matter. We have taken the liberty to use the alternate translation "with" for the Hebrew prefix translated "in" by the NASB.

"He makes the *[dark]* clouds His chariot" (Ps. 104: 3b, emphasis added).

The second snapshot pictures God making clouds his chariot. To paraphrase this clause, he made dark clouds his transport device for the separated fluids. Here we have taken the liberty to use an alternate translation of the Hebrew word translated as clouds by replacing it with dark clouds. It is the same word used to describe the thick, dark cloud that hid the glory of God from the Israelites in the wilderness (Ex. 19:9). To hide God's glory took an especially dark and thick cloud that may not be found naturally in the Earth's atmosphere. That cloud was most likely a supernaturally formed cloud.

In the context of this verse, the clouds are extraordinary in that they are appointed as God's chariot. As discussed in the next chapter, the atmosphere of Earth was not formed until the beginning of the third day. So these dark clouds could not have been ordinary atmospheric clouds. Instead, they most likely were supernaturally formed for the purpose of transporting something different than molecular water, and they would have existed in extraterrestrial space.

Historically, chariots were transportation for hosts of soldiers in an army going into battle. From the context of this verse, we infer that God used supernaturally formed dark clouds to transport the separated fluid droplets to their future locations in the heavens. Later, he transformed all these fluid droplets into the physical hosts of heaven.

"He walks upon the *[edges]* of the wind" (Ps. 104:3c, emphasis added).

The third snapshot pictured God walking on the edges of the wind. The word *edges* is an alternative translation of the Hebrew word translated as *wings* by the NASB. It gives a better physical description of the event that was involved in this clause since winds don't have wings. In Old Testament times, putting something under one's feet symbolized the power and total control that a person had over those things (Ps. 8:6, 47:3). In the context of this verse, we infer that God had total control of the "wind," which he also creates (Amos 4:13). Here the wind may have been the supernatural forces that propelled the dark-cloud chariots to their new locations in the universe. This verse may have previewed God's direct control over the supernatural winds, his angels, described by the following snapshot.

"He makes the winds His messengers, flaming fire His ministers" (Ps. 104:4).

The physical events described in the Old Testament, in language that seems to fit the context in literal terms, may sometimes be interpreted in a supernatural way by a verse in the New Testament. The physical events are true, but then there is also a true supernatural explanation behind them. Verse 4 may be just such a case.

The verse contains a parallelism that described the same event on the second day with God using two physical means to build the universe. To paraphrase the verse, he made winds his delivery agents (messengers) and flaming fire his servant.

Most people have seen raging infernos, such as a large building or a forest on fire, where the winds whip the flames into small tornados. The language of verse 4 suggests just such a picture. However, the windy flames in this snapshot are doing God's bidding. Therefore they are his messengers (sent ones, the normal word for *angels*) and his servants (responding to his orders).

In the previous verse, God has distributed his dark-cloud chariots carrying the physical heavenly hosts throughout the universe-in-making. The formation of those thick, dark clouds and their spreading out has caused the universe to go dark (relatively) for the evening and night of the second day. But then, out of these chariots come winds of flaming fire; morning has broken on the dawn of the second day.

Now, what does the New Testament reveal about the supernatural causes behind this event? Consider Hebrews 1:7, which contains a direct quote of Psalm 104:4, "And of the angels He says, "Who makes [appoints] His angels winds and His ministers a flame of fire." This New Testament quote actually uses the translated words in the same order as they appear in the Hebrew text of the psalm. To paraphrase the quote in Hebrews 1:7, he appoints his angels as winds and his servants as a flame of fire.

However, the significant difference in Hebrews 1:7 is that its context unmistakably refers to "angelic beings" as the "messengers" and "ministers" doing God's bidding. This tells the reader more about Psalm 104:4, namely, that the winds of flaming fire were not just acting on their own, due to natural forces, but that they were being caused and controlled by angelic beings—God's messengers or helpers. The angels were helping construct exactly the universe God had designed.

We infer that the role of angels controlling winds and flaming fire most likely refers to their use of winds and fire in the formation and positioning of the celestial bodies in all the galaxies of the universe. In this manner the celestial bodies remained in fluid form, either gaseous or a molten liquid due to the flames, until they reached their locations in the heavens driven by the winds.

In summary, this snapshot showed God's great power and majesty in the control of the angels that he had created, presumably when he set up the heavens as his kingdom (Ps. 103:19–23). These verses complimented Psalm 103 with the description of specific roles for the angels that carried out his commands on the second day. One can find more support for the presence of angels during creation week and the making of the heavens and Earth in Job 38:7.

Divine Action 3: Separating the Waters and Making the Expanse

"He established the earth upon its foundations, so that it will not totter forever and ever" (Ps. 104:5).

This verse describes a snapshot of God laying the foundations of the planet Earth. This alludes to the CMA where it stated: "and [God] separated the waters which were below the expanse from the waters which were above [in] the expanse" (Gen. 1:7, emphasis added). The fluids below became the core, mantle, and crust of the planet. The majority of these foundations have remained a fluid of molten rock. We have taken the liberty to insert the word *in* from the prefix of the Hebrew word translated *expanse* that the NASB does not include. The last clause of this verse states that the planet we call Earth was made to last until the end of time.

Job 26:7

He stretches out the north over empty space and hangs the earth on nothing.
—Job 26:7

This verse is one of many in chapter 26 of Job that gave a description of some wondrous act of God (v. 14 calls these acts "fringes of His ways"). To paraphrase the verse, God *spread out* the northern sky *against* empty space and hung the [planet Earth] on nothing. Here, we took the liberty to use alternate translations for the words translated in the NASB as *stretches out* and *over*. Job most likely referred to God making nearly empty space between the planet Earth and all the other celestial bodies on the second day when he separated the waters below from those above in the stretched-out heavens (Gen. 1:7). Job continued this description by God hanging the planet Earth on nothing but empty space after it had formed into a sphere.

The finished product that Job described in this verse was the planet separated, at least visibly, from all the other celestial bodies in the universe by an expanse of space. From the viewpoint of a person on the surface of a planet, this accurately described that planet's position in the heavens. It complemented verse 7 of the CMA where it was reported that the expanse separated "waters which were below" (referring to the planet) from the "waters which were above" (referring to the other physical hosts of heaven).

More General References

Besides the detailed descriptions in Psalm 104 and Job 26, there are numerous other references to the stretching out and spreading out of the heavens. These can be found in Job 9:8, 37:18; Isaiah 40:22, 42:5, 44:24, 45:12, 48:13, 51:13; Jeremiah 10:12, 51:15; and Zechariah 12:1. All these references firmly support the words of the CMA, Psalm 104, and Job 26 on the products of God's third miracle.

There was also a reference to God leading forth and individually calling the stars by name in Isaiah 40:26 when he stretched out the heavens. In Job 9:7, God also commands the sun and stars not to shine at some time in the history of the world. Perhaps this was after they were made on the second day but remained only proto-stars (not giving off visible light) until the fourth day.

SCIENTIFIC TERMINOLOGY

Space

The author of the CMA reported that God formed the expanse in close relationship to the separated fluid droplets (waters) of primordial earth. Genesis 1:6 used the word *midst* to describe this relationship. This expanse separated fluid droplets from fluid droplets. In modern scientific terms, the expanse would be the space that separates all the celestial spheres of matter from each other in the universe. Scientists have found that space consists mainly of a vacuum. However, they have discovered that it contains both EMR and a small amount of atomic matter in the form of clouds of interstellar or intergalactic media (IGM), but at very low concentrations. They have also found that almost everywhere in the vacuum of space there are both electromagnetic and gravitational force fields. The force fields are located in space but originate and terminate in the clumps of atomic matter that make up the stars, planets, and moons.

White Holes or Quasars?

Since scientists have never claimed to observe a white hole, it remains only a theoretical construct. Theoretically, white holes act like black holes in reverse. Instead of pulling matter and EMR into their event horizons and expanding, the white holes eject both into the space around them, thereby shrinking the event horizon of the black hole in which they developed. Most cosmologists/astronomers have claimed that white holes never existed even though they are allowed as a solution to the equations of general relativity. White holes are a special solution of those equations and could only have existed if they formed under unique conditions.

The conditions that would be required to form white holes point to a creation model simply because they have not been shown to occur naturally. For this reason, white holes haven't been included in any evolutionary cosmology or model. It is also the reason why most scientists believe they never existed. For a more detailed discussion of white holes and the theory that predicts them from a creationist perspective, see *Starlight and Time* by D. Russell Humphreys.[2]

Astronomers have observed, however, what they have called quasi-stellar radio objects or quasars. These objects are EMR sources that are many times brighter than whole galaxies of stars found near them. The quasars that are close enough to observe from Earth in detail have been found in the center of a galaxy. If quasars are at the same distance from Earth as the remainder of the galaxy around them, they emit a tremendous amount of energy from a relatively small area in that galaxy. Their energy output has been measured to be as great as 10 trillion times the output of the sun. They have expended so much energy for their size that astronomers believe they could only have obtained that energy from a black hole. There is nothing else in the universe known to mankind that could supply the amount of energy required to power such a small bright object for the length of time that quasars have been observed. The first quasar was discovered and identified as an astronomical object in 1961, and that quasar is still observable today.

If black holes do supply the energy for quasars, it is possible that a given quasar may have resulted from an ultra-massive black hole. This could have taken place by white holes developing in its event horizon. One known characteristic of a quasar—an intense focused beam of EMR—is theoretically also a characteristic of a white hole. But because quasars have been found only at such great distances (billions of light years) from Earth, it has been difficult to determine whether or not they also eject the atomic matter that forms stars, planets, and moons. However, recent observations have revealed the absorption spectra of some solid compounds from the area around the edges of a quasar.

Quasars resemble white holes that have been significantly reduced in magnitude and possibly slowed in their rate of EMR emission and atomic matter ejection. They could have remained after an ultra-massive black hole ejected most of the atomic matter and EMR through white holes while forming its galaxy. For more information on quasars and their being the source of galaxies and stars see *Seeing Red* by Halton Arp.[3]

Primordial Celestial Spheres

In the context of this book, primordial celestial spheres refer to the separated clumps of fluid matter that formed spheres of all the proto-stars, proto-planets, and spherical moons due to their own gravity. From the perspective of the CMA, these spheres of atomic matter were made from the primordial earth blob and placed in the expanse of space that separates them from the planet Earth. A sampling of different-sized celestial spheres is shown in Illustration 4.1.

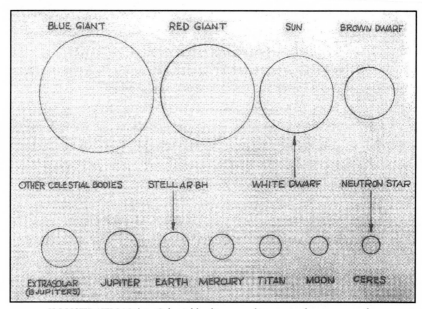

ILLUSTRATION 4.1: Celestial bodies according to size but not to scale.

Divine Action 3: Separating the Waters and Making the Expanse

Galaxies

Galaxies have been called islands in the sea of space. They got this designation because they are large groups of stars separated from other groups by great distances. Earth is located in an orbit around a star (the sun) in the Milky Way galaxy. The Milky Way galaxy is only one of billions of galaxies that have been discovered since the invention of the telescope. Only one or two galaxies are close enough to Earth to be visible without a telescope. Astronomers have classified all the known galaxies into the three categories of spiral, elliptical, and irregular based on their structural appearance.

Primordial Planet

The most generalized definition of a planet has historically been a celestial sphere that orbits a star. There are four types of planets found in the solar system. The four inner planets are considered terrestrial because they consist mainly of solid and liquid compounds with only a small proportion of gases. Next in distance from the sun, there are two planets considered gas giants because they consist mainly of gaseous compounds with a small liquid and/or solid core. The outer two major planets are considered ice giants because they consist of large icy bodies covered by relatively thin atmospheres.

The other planets in the solar system, discovered more recently, are called dwarf planets. Mainly located beyond the orbits of the major planets, they are made of frozen liquid and gaseous compounds. One rocky dwarf planet (Ceres) is located in the asteroid belt between the orbits of Mars and Jupiter. The total number of dwarf planets is not known as more are still being discovered beyond the orbit of Neptune.

THE CM-MODEL

As described in the previous two chapters, God's first two actions or miracles created a primitive and as yet unrecognizable universe. In the CM-model at the end of the first day, this universe consisted of a large 4-D space-time continuum and a relatively small and formless blob of a mixture of EMR, atomic matter (most likely in the form of plasma), and some remaining perfect fluid.

The separation of light and darkness reported in the CMA by the end of the first day led to speculation that the blob contained volumes of darkness interspersed with volumes of light. Furthermore, both the volumes of light and darkness contained a fluid consisting of EMR, atomic matter, and the universal substance a perfect fluid. The volumes of darkness took on the characteristics of black holes as they grew and collected atomic matter, EMR, and some perfect fluid into their event horizons.

Divine Act 3

Let there be an expanse between droplets of the blob of transitory fluids, and let it separate fluid droplets from fluid droplets.
—Gen. 1:6, paraphrased

The author of the CMA reported, in general terms, the processes and physical products resulting from God's third action on the second day. We infer from verse 8 of the CMA that this event took place in two phases. The first phase took place during the night and the second phase provided the visible light for the second half of the day.

Phase 1—Evening of Day 2

As stated above, the blob of fluid was already separated into volumes of light and darkness. For the model, we speculate that in the first phase of miracle 3, God separated the dark volumes from within the blob into billions of ultra-massive black holes. He then moved these black holes to locations where they were distributed throughout the universe and separated by great distances.

This separation and stretching out process resulted in the formation of the expanse that contained the waters above, as reported in verse 7 of the CMA. Darkness for the nighttime period of the second day resulted because the separation of the large masses of the black holes also stretched out the EMR and gravity force fields that were located between them. Most of the visible light outside the black holes was stretched into long wavelength radiation, so it became invisible. This model of what took place follows the sequence of snapshots found in Psalm 104:2–4.

Divine Action 3: Separating the Waters and Making the Expanse

God's purpose for separating and moving the black holes apart was given in Psalm 104:2b–3. He did it to stretch out the expanse and form the large-scale structure of the heavens. This included transporting the fluids within black holes (dark clouds as his chariot) to their destinations throughout the universe where galaxies are observed today. Most of these fluids were destined to become the hosts of heaven (stars) two days later.

Scientifically, it took a huge force to cause the ultra-massive black holes to move apart while stretching out the gravitational fields that attracted them to each other. The same principle is demonstrated when two opposite magnetic poles are pulled apart resulting in a stretched magnetic field between them (Illustration 3.3, bottom-attraction view). We assume that God supplied the necessary force. Psalm 104:3 states that God shows great power in his total control (walks on the edges) of the wind. The definition of wind given earlier was matter put in collective motion by some force. We speculate that the wind on the second day was the supernatural means God used to move the black holes to their destinations. Verse 4 of the psalm supports this concept by appointing angels as winds.

The resulting structure of space is recognized today by the array of galaxies and galaxy clusters distributed throughout the observable universe. Astronomers call this the large-scale structure of the universe. Each galaxy consists of a large number (billions) of stars including many star clusters, numerous interstellar gas and dust clouds, and possibly a smaller but still super-massive black hole at its center. Stellar systems have been found that contain up to four stars; others contain only one star with multiple planets and their moons. It is possible that all stellar systems may contain asteroids and comets similar to Earth's solar system, although they are presently unobservable.

For the CM-model, we speculate that the atomic matter in all the celestial spheres in each galaxy initially came out of the ultra-massive black hole from which the galaxy was formed. By surveying detectable galaxies in three dimensions, astronomers have shown that they are arranged in a large web-like structure as shown in Illustration 4.2.

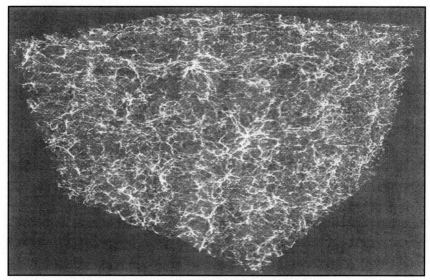

ILLUSTRATION 4.2: Artist's concept of a portion of the
universe showing its structure of galaxies.

This cosmic view resulted from an artist using actual measurement data
of location and distance to the galaxies in that portion of the universe.
The webbing is formed by strings of lighted galaxies (a point of light is
a galaxy in the illustration) that surround large dark volumes of space
separating them. What the dark volumes of space contain, if anything,
hasn't been discovered. When viewed from an even broader perspective
through computer simulation, the universe appears as a single gigantic
cloud of galaxies.

Atomic Matter Formation

For the CM-model, we speculated that some original perfect fluid
remained in the mixture of fluids within the ultra-massive black holes.
Any atomic matter that was contained in the black holes most likely
remained in plasma form because of the temperatures and pressures
that are theoretically part of the black hole's internal environment. As
explained previously, plasma was a gaseous state of matter that consisted
of atomic element nuclei, their ions, and many free electrons.

Previously in the CM-model, atoms of lower atomic number were
formed at the same time as light. Clouds of atomic elements with atomic

number up to 18 have been detected residing in space between galaxies. We speculate that these clouds of elements originated and remained outside the ultra-massive black holes as they were separated.

Atomic elements of atomic number higher than 18 can be explained as forming inside the black holes by a process called nucleosynthesis. Nucleosynthesis is a combination of fusion and fission of two or more nuclei that resulted in the nucleus of a different element. First, lower atomic number nuclei are fused to build a nucleus of a higher atomic number element. But to form nuclei of odd atomic number, nuclei of higher atomic number have to split by nuclear fission into elements of the lower, odd atomic numbers. A general description of the nucleosynthesis process for forming the main elements of Earth was given by Dr. Edward Boudreaux in an appendix titled "Origins of Chemical Elements" that can be found in the book *Radioisotopes and the Age of the Earth*.[4]

It took temperatures of over 10 billion Kelvins for some of the fusion and fission processes involved. Those temperatures are theoretically possible in an ultra-massive black hole. For comparison, in the Big Bang model it was postulated that the necessary temperatures and pressures for nucleosynthesis occur in the explosions of large stars called supernova. Theoretically the temperatures and pressures that could be reached in large star explosions would be much less than those possible within a gigantic black hole.

Phase 2—Dawn of Day 2

"God made the expanse, and separated the transitory fluids which were below the expanse from the transitory fluid droplets which were above in the expanse" (Gen. 1:7, paraphrased).

The source of light for the daylight hours of the second day was not identified in the CMA. But it was reported that daylight existed on that day just like any other normal day (v. 8). Included in the CM-model is a natural process that God could have used to light up the universe at dawn of the second day based on Psalm 104:4. We speculate that a second phase of separation took place once the ultra-massive black holes reached their destinations.

This second phase involved the transformation of the ultra-massive black holes into one of several white hole configurations. These white holes then emitted visible radiation and ejected great amounts of white-hot gaseous and liquid matter into space around the black hole. The ejected atomic matter formed all the celestial spheres, dust clouds, and gas clouds that surrounded any remaining black hole at the center of the resulting galaxy. This emission of massive amounts of EMR and ejection of white-hot molten matter would have been the source that provided the light for the daylight portion of the second day.

Galaxy Formation

For the CM-model, we speculate that each ultra-massive black hole developed one or more white holes in its event horizon through which a galaxy was formed around the black hole. Most galaxies retained a relatively smaller but still super-massive black hole at their center after the galaxy had formed. Psalm 104:4 pictured God appointing his angels as winds and flaming fire to do his bidding. A white hole would represent the source of the greatest wind and hottest fire imaginable since it consisted of fission and fusion processes as found in nuclear explosions. The angels could have been the supernatural cause of all the white holes. These holes all occurred on the same day and at the same time throughout the universe following God's direction.

With the reasonable speculation that some perfect fluid was enclosed within the ultra-massive black holes, a physical explanation can be offered for the white holes. The white holes in the event horizons formed when enough remaining perfect fluid was transformed into EMR and atomic matter inside the black hole after it had been separated from the other black holes. The rapid transformation of the perfect fluid into atoms, and the resultant expansion into plasma, created the internal pressure required to breach the black hole's event horizon. These breaches of the event horizon then formed the white holes through which the EMR and atomic matter escaped. The process would have been similar to filling a balloon with water until it bursts to relieve the pressure. However, some black holes burst only at particular locations on the surface of their event horizons rather than suffering a total collapse of that entire horizon.

As mentioned above, astronomers have discovered three general types of galaxies and have placed them into the categories of spiral, elliptical, and irregular. We speculate that they were formed by three different configurations of white holes.

Divine Action 3: Separating the Waters and Making the Expanse

Elliptical

An elliptical galaxy could have formed from a single, almost spherically symmetric, white hole—a total collapse (at least temporarily) of the entire event horizon. This white hole ejected matter and EMR simultaneously in every direction, much like starburst fireworks. Whether this type of galaxy retained a smaller black hole at the center hasn't been resolved by observations at this time. Astronomers have recently found that elliptical galaxies are few in number relative to spiral galaxies.

Spiral

A spiral galaxy would have resulted when two or more white holes formed on different points of a black hole event horizon and caused it to spin. The jets of energy and matter left at a right angle to this spin axis. The streams of molten matter and hot gases mapped out a spiral pattern much like a rotating lawn sprinkler, as shown in Illustration 4.3, until the streams out of the white holes were stopped. The matter and energy leaving through the white holes caused the black hole to rotate on an axis that is oriented in a single direction and thereby

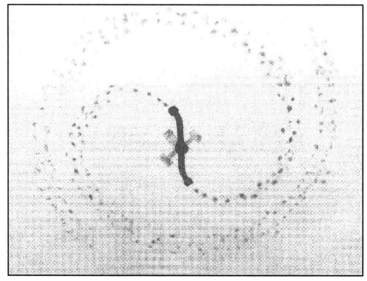

ILLUSTRATION 4.3: Rotating lawn sprinkler demonstrating spiral galaxy formation.

formed the galaxy disk in a plane at right angle to the axis. The arms in spiral galaxies most likely continued to rotate about this axis after the galaxy-forming actions had been completed. The streams of atomic matter broke up into droplets that formed all the stars, planets, and moons, within that galaxy.

Irregular

An irregular galaxy could have formed by combinations of single, double, or other white-hole configurations. There are a myriad of possible scenarios, each of which could have produced an interesting pattern or seeming non-pattern. And there is no reason to believe or suggest that any configuration that has been observed would have been more likely to form. Here again the great power and majesty of God was expressed in simple and understandable physical terms (Is. 40:26) that are ignored by scientists who support evolution.

Milky Way Galaxy

The CMA, for obvious reasons, was written to focus on the preparation of the universe, and especially the planet Earth, for human habitation. Therefore, it is reasonable to assume that God moved all the other black holes away from the black hole that would form the Milky Way galaxy where Earth resides. For this reason, in the CM-model we positioned the Milky Way in a preferred location at or near the center of the universe. God formed the Milky Way galaxy as a barred spiral that is approximately 100,000 light years in diameter and 3,000 light years in thickness. The spiral structure is shown in Illustration 4.4 from a cosmic perspective looking down on the galaxy. In that view the whole galaxy is rotating clockwise around its center where there is a super-massive black hole. The bar of the spiral is located near the center of the galaxy, and it represents the connection between rotating emitters in the analogy of the lawn sprinkler. The ends of the bar are the possible locations of the white holes, and they may appear as quasars now if they could be observed from Earth. They are not visible from Earth because they are pointed in directions away from it.

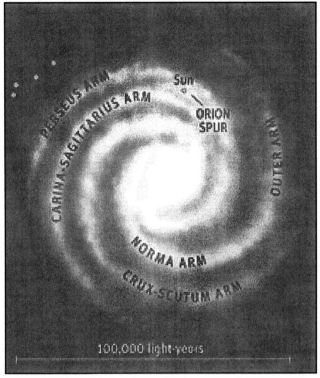

ILLUSTRATION 4.4: Artist's concept of the structure of the Milky Way galaxy.

The sun and its planets, including Earth, formed a solar system that is located in the galaxy approximately midway between the outer edge and a central bulge that formed around the center of the galaxy. That bulge is approximately 3,000 light years in diameter. In total, astronomers estimate there are approximately 400 billion visible stars in the Milky Way. With all its stellar systems, its gas and dust clouds, and its central core, the mass has been estimated to be 600 billion times the mass of the sun.

A spherical black hole containing the mass of the Milky Way would have had an event horizon with a radius of approximately two-tenths of a light year. In the CM-model, the jet streams of atomic matter (plasma and magma) and EMR would have traveled out from this small radius to the edge of the galaxy 50,000 light years away in less than three days. It had to occur prior to the fourth day when the stars were completed and they were fixed in their relative locations. The formation of the Milky

Way could only have been possible if the proto-stars, proto-planets, and moons were transported by supernatural means. Both matter and light must have been moving at speeds many times faster than the speed of light as measured today. Scientists call such speeds superluminal and have found that they are impossible to attain on or near Earth.

The magnificent acts of forming the universe and the individual galaxies must be considered the supernatural acts of an all-powerful God and possibly utilizing his mighty angels (Ps. 103:20). Natural processes couldn't supply the energy and forces required to build the universe, even if there was an infinite amount of time. Scientists who support evolution have attempted to explain this lack of natural resources by inventing such items as quantum fluctuations, dark energy, and dark matter. But no one has been able to find any of these items or even determine theoretically what they are.

Celestial Sphere Formation

After being ejected from the white hole, the plasma and molten magma cooled due to its rapid motion away from the energy source and its dispersion into a larger volume of space. As they cooled, they formed into spherical globules of high temperature fluids (liquids and gases) due to their own gravity. These fluids were a mixture of the atomic elements and their various chemical compounds that occur naturally everywhere in the universe. The globules formed individual spheres due to the equalization of their internal pressure and the force of their gravitational field. They became the primordial celestial spheres that were initially the proto-stars, proto-planets, and spherical moons. By the end of the second day, the molten fluid globules had cooled to begin forming the basic internal structures of their type of celestial sphere.

Scientifically, the term *below* is commonly used to describe something that is closer to the center of gravity of Earth than the object it is under. But in general, Earth can be replaced as the reference by any large mass of atomic matter with its own gravity, such as a star, another planet, or even a moon. The phrase "waters which were below the expanse" at this point (v. 7) in the CMA timeline could have referred to any and all spheres of gaseous or liquid atomic matter that had formed, each with its own gravitational field. The Earth is the most familiar example of the waters below, because mankind live on it, and God chose it as our reference. If people lived on Mars, they would perceive their planet to have been made of the waters below, because Mars would have been their reference.

The proto-stars, proto-planets, and moons formed from different mixtures of the atomic elements and compounds depending on where their material originated in the white hole, how much gathered together into their droplet of fluid matter, its location in the jet stream or wind, and when that portion of the jet stream left the white hole. All the atomic matter of the planets and moons in the solar system must have exited the white hole near enough to the sun so they could be captured in its gravitational field during the journey to their present location in the Milky Way galaxy.

We speculate that once the spheres had formed, they would have cooled rapidly during the remainder of the day while they continued to emit EMR to light the universe. They shrank in size as they cooled and took on their final spherical shapes. Each began its rotation on its axis, thereby generating its magnetic field, if God designed it to have one. God had determined their composition of solids, liquids, and gases, as well as their size (Job 38:5), while they were on their journey and still in fluid form.

Proto-stars

Based on further speculation, the proto-stars cooled down to temperatures that provided little visible light at the end of the second day. They may have responded to God's command to stop shining (Job 9:7). In physical terms, they remained mainly gaseous but only began to form their complex internal structure and their magnetic fields. Their internal nuclear fusion and fission processes did not reach ignition temperatures and pressures until two days later when God commanded them to become the light providers. These proto-stars could be referred to as gigantic gaseous planets. They had the characteristics of brown dwarf stars that still exist in most galaxies today. They may have been the "morning stars" referred to in Job 38:7 that "sang together" with the angels at the founding of Earth.

Proto-planet Earth

The proto-planet that became Earth was formed along with every other proto-star, proto-planet, and spherical moon. As a terrestrial planet, it had a hot solid and liquid core, a thick molten rock mantle, and a relatively thin solidifying crust, as shown in Illustration 4.5. We speculate that as the planet cooled, more chemical compounds were formed into solids, liquids, and gases in chambers under the surface of the crust. At the high temperatures of molten magma, chemical compounds like water, carbon dioxide, ammonia, and hydrocarbons such as methane and propane wouldn't form from their atomic elements if they were exposed to open space. They required much higher pressure at molten rock temperatures than supplied by even a normal atmosphere. These pressures were only possible beneath the surface as the planet cooled. The gaseous and liquid compounds would have formed in pockets in the crust-like blisters that form under the outer skin.

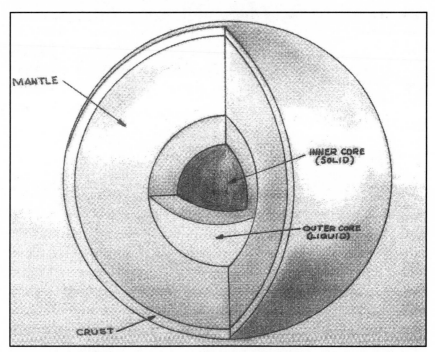

ILLUSTRATION 4.5: Artist's concept of the internal structure of planet Earth.

For example, the formation of water molecules releases a tremendous amount of energy in the form of heat. This energy had to be transferred away from the steam, or it would have returned to its constituent gases of hydrogen and oxygen. The surrounding rock would have absorbed this extra heat energy and then transferred it to the surface where it could radiate directly into space.

Theoretically, the magnetic field of a planet resulted from the different rotation rate of solid magnetic material like iron and nickel in an inner core plus electrical-conducting liquid rock of an outer core. The inner core needed to be a solid for it to form a permanent magnet with both a north and a south pole. The electrical charges in the molten liquid of the outer core as it flowed around this solid inner core generated the planetary magnetic field. The design and construction of planet Earth, so that it formed an optimum magnetic field, was not an accident. It demonstrated again the power and wisdom of the Great Designer and Builder.

The scientists who support evolution have found it difficult to explain how Earth could have retained a solid and liquid core with its magnetic field for 4.5 billion years. They claim that Earth formed that long ago. The planet required a magnetic field to protect its surface habitat from harmful high-energy radiation and particles that exist everywhere in space ever since it was formed. Without the protection of the magnetic field, living creatures could not exist on this planet.

SCIENTIFIC EVIDENCE THAT SUPPORTS THE CM-MODEL

Common Elements Found Throughout the Universe

The most obvious evidence scientists have discovered that supports the CM-model is the universal distribution of the same atomic matter and EMR throughout the universe. The celestial spheres are all made from the atomic elements found in the periodic table and are held together by the same EMR frequencies that are emitted and absorbed on Earth. We infer from this universe-wide evidence that there was a single source and, since nothing existed before time started, it was supplied by the supernatural Creator and Maker of this universe.

In his third miracle, God distributed and positioned the galaxies that form the large-scale structure of the universe. He used fluid-like atomic matter as building blocks and stretched out the force fields as mortar that holds the universe together. They formed the web-like structure detected on the largest scale that can be measured in the heavens today. The billions upon billions of celestial spheres in the billions of galaxies are all made from some combination of the atomic elements of the periodic table. No new atomic elements have been found anywhere in extraterrestrial space.

Besides the atomic matter, astronomers have detected every frequency of EMR originating in space and some even between the galaxies. These observations provide scientific evidence that supports speculation in the CM-model for events on the second day. Based on reasonable speculation, the interpretation of this evidence placed everything found between galaxies outside the event horizons of the ultra-massive black holes. It was left behind when the black holes were separated and moved to their final locations. The whole gravitational and EMR environment of the atoms and molecules left behind were changed. These changes can be studied by looking at the evidence in space between galaxies and star systems. The questions of what atomic matter and EMR are present between the galaxies and how it got there are current topics of astronomical investigation. The CM-model provides simple and realistic answers to these questions that involve God using his great power during creation week.

Scientists Located IGM

Astronomers have found streams of high-temperature ion clouds in intergalactic space and have called it intergalactic media (IGM). These IGM plasma clouds have been detected and identified by the x-ray and ultra-violet radiation spectrums they absorb from the light of distant quasar sources. All detected quasar sources are located great distances from the Milky Way galaxy and can be observed in almost any direction from Earth. Ions identified by these spectral absorption measurements include the elements argon, carbon, neon, nitrogen, and oxygen.[5] These elements have an atomic number from 12 to 18.

The spectrum of the radiation that they absorb also indicated the ions of these elements are at a temperature in the range from 100,000 to 10 million K. The average temperature on the surface of Earth is around 300 K. The sun's average surface temperature is approximately 6,000 K. So these ion clouds have retained a significantly higher temperature than the average 3 K of the space surrounding them. They remained much hotter than the surface of the sun that actively generates its own heat. Evolutionary scientists have not answered the question of how these temperatures can be retained by ion clouds without an energy source. They claim that the clouds have been there for billions of years based on their proposed age of the universe and the galaxies. However, this recently observed evidence definitely points to a much younger age for the clouds and therefore the whole universe.

Astronomers have also eliminated the possibility that the ion clouds reside inside the Milky Way galaxy where they could obtain some energy from its stars. They have measured the position of the EMR spectral lines within the absorption spectrum relative to that spectrum found on Earth. They found that the spectral lines absorbed by the IGM are not Doppler-shifted the same amount as the lines measured for the same elements in the stars of the Milky Way galaxy or absorbed by ion clouds within the galaxy. This data has shown that the IGM is moving much slower relative to Earth than the rotation of the galaxy allows.

This slower motion caused the spectral lines to be shifted more toward the red end of the visible spectrum. This red shifting of spectral lines is caused by the same type of Doppler-shifting that causes train whistles to have a different sound frequency when the train is approaching versus when it is leaving. The ions in the IGM are definitely moving away from Earth and not moving with the velocity of everything else within the Milky Way galaxy. The ions therefore have to be located in the space between our galaxy and the quasar radiation sources.

Scientists Located the Source of CMBR

Besides the atomic matter of the IGM in space, modern astronomers have found EMR from space that they have named cosmic microwave background radiation (CMBR). The CMBR is recognized by a continuous frequency spectrum (containing no detectable spectral lines), which has a peak intensity value in the microwave portion of the EMR spectrum. The location of the spectrum peak is equivalent to that radiated by atomic matter at a temperature of 2.7 K.

In the standard cosmology model, scientists who support evolution proposed that this radiation was emitted as visible radiation approximately 300 thousand years after the Big Bang. They explained its peak value by claiming it had been Doppler-shifted by the expansion of space in the universe over the more than 13 billion years since that time. The amount that the CMBR peak has been shifted is estimated at 1,000 times, so the peak frequency supposedly originated in a universe where the average temperature of atomic matter was at approximately 3,000 K or less than the temperature of the surface of the sun.

But recent measurements[6] of the CMBR showed that the radiation could not have originated at the distance of 13 billion light years that the Big Bang theory requires. The CMBR in the direction of nearby galaxies does not show any variations due to shadows that should be caused by these galaxies. Shadowing would be expected if the radiation source were behind these galaxies. It can be inferred from this recent measurement data that the source of CMBR is between the nearer galaxies and Earth. If it was not originally spread out uniformly everywhere in space, it must have originated in the space between galaxies.

CM-Model Explains the Location of IGM and CMBR

Both the ion clouds and background radiation sources can be simply explained by the CM-model. They resulted from atomic matter and EMR that were outside the event horizons of the ultra-massive black holes when God separated the black holes to form the expanse of space. The atomic matter remained in high-temperature plasma clouds that have retained a significant level of that temperature for the thousands of years since creation.

The EMR that escaped into space from the blob could have contained much higher frequencies and therefore higher energy before the separation of the black holes. The separation would have stretched out (Doppler-shifted) the EMR. All this would have happened in a very short time compared to the 13 billion years of the Big Bang model. The author of the CMA reported the start of the primordial earth blob separation at the beginning of the second day (vv. 6–8), and the heavens, including all the stars, were completed by the end of fourth day (vv. 17–19).

White Holes Cannot Be Excluded

There is no direct evidence that white holes existed at the beginning of the universe. However, scientists have found evidence that quasars are powered by black holes and that they reside in the far reaches of the universe. This evidence implies quasars existed in the early universe, or they would not be observed today. Astronomers have also found that these quasars are visible because the EMR they emit is directed toward Earth like a beacon from a lighthouse. We infer that these quasars are the remnants of white holes that happened to stop their rotation pointing toward Earth. We mentioned earlier that quasars emit high intensity EMR and that black holes are the only possible source for the amount of power being expended. Some astronomers have speculated that they may also eject atomic matter. The most recent data has supported this speculation. It has not been verified because the long distances to quasars make observation of relatively small liquid or solid matter clumps nearly impossible.

Halton Arp, in his book *Seeing Red*, has challenged the Big Bang model with observational evidence that older galaxies gave birth to new galaxies by ejecting matter at high velocities from their galactic centers.[7] Galactic centers are where super-massive black holes exist today, as observed in many nearby galaxies. That is also the location of all the quasars that are close enough to Earth so that their source galaxy can be observed. If super-massive black holes power all the detected quasars, it is reasonable to speculate that the black holes are also their origin. Therefore, quasars may be the remnants of the white holes that have a significantly decreased EMR and atomic matter output after they completed their purpose, forming the galaxies around them. It is also possible that in the Milky Way galaxy, quasars could still exist at the ends of the mid-galactic bar. They cannot be observed because they ended up pointing away from Earth.

Rapidly Cooling Solid Matter

In the CM-model, the ejected atomic matter cooled on the journey to its location in the galaxy because it expanded into a larger volume of nearly empty space. Based on reasonable speculation, small eddies could have formed, causing whirlpools that separated the matter inside the eddy from nearby plasma and other droplets of fluid matter. Then the cooling and condensing of the whirlpool action would have turned the hot fluid into a mixture of gaseous and molten liquid compounds. The composition of matter in these whirlpools determined the type of celestial sphere that formed in them. The relative positions of the various celestial spheres determined the configuration of the stellar systems that resulted.

Once positioned in the planetary system of the sun, the molten fluid droplet that became the planet Earth rapidly cooled further. It was also drawn into a spherical form by its own gravity while still rotating on its axis from the eddy in which it formed. On its surface, where heat radiated directly into the surrounding space, the molten rock turned rapidly into a solid, because liquids and gases would have escaped into the vacuum of space. Within the sphere, concentric shells of liquid and solid rock began to form what could be called the foundations of the planet. The core and mantle remained at higher temperatures and mainly in a molten fluid form. The outer surface turned into solid crust that contained chambers of liquid and gaseous chemical compounds.

Evidence of rapid cooling in the crust has been recently discovered on Earth within crystals in rocks. Crystals grow at a temperature where a fluid compound turns into a solid. A recent study report by creation scientists on the radioisotopes of uranium (U) and polonium (Po) in crystals within rocks revealed that both elements formed radio halos within the same solid crystalline material called biotite.[8] The radio halos of the two elements were found at separated sites in the same crystal.

Radio halos are damaged crystals around places where radioactive impurities are found. Polonium is a short-lived product from radioactive decay of ^{238}U. The first polonium daughter product (^{218}Po) that results has a half-life of 3.1 minutes. The average distance between the U radio halo site and the Po site was 1 millimeter. The Po would have had to move to its new site from the U site where it had formed in less than a few minutes while the molten rock retained enough liquid to transport it. The molten rock also had to turn into a solid before any radio halos could have begun to form.

The conclusion that we draw from this data is summarized in a quote by one of the research physicists involved in the study: "Much of the hydrothermal fluid which transports and relocates the isotopes is generated as the magma crystallizes. The presence of the short-lived polonium halos indicates that the magma cooled to solid rock very rapidly rather than over long ages as often assumed."[9]

This evidence also implies that radioactive processes were accelerated during the formation of the rocks in the crust of the planet. The products of the nuclear decay of uranium occurred in just a few minutes and did not take millions or billions of years like they would have at their recently measured rates. Only God's supernatural power could have caused such a nuclear-process rate-increase that produced the radio halos in such a short time. This is another demonstration of the rapid maturing of the created universe during the first four days of creation week.

SUMMARY

Once an experienced contractor decides to build a structure, he begins by having an architect design it. As part of the design, the architect would choose the materials that met the design requirements for each individual part of the structure. Then the contractor would obtain the materials the design required to build the structure. After he has obtained the materials, he builds the structure by placing the correct materials in their designed locations. This same procedure is the only reasonable explanation for the large-scaled structure of the universe, as discovered by mankind's scientific investigations. It should be obvious to everyone that it did not build itself like the supporters of evolution believe.

The CM-model reflects this construction process, with God as the architect and builder. In the model, the nighttime of the second day corresponded with the separation of the primordial earth blob into many ultra-massive black holes formed from a fluid-like substance. These black holes contained large quantities of atomic matter, EMR, and some remaining perfect fluid. God then used these black holes to transport the fluid-like matter and EMR to the present location of galaxies in the universe.

In a second phase of separation, God transformed each of these black holes into one of at least three white-hole configurations to form galaxies. As noted above, all this may have been done with the support of his angels. The details of how it was done are mainly speculation because it was done by supernatural means. There are presently no experiments or even realistic computer simulations that can be used to demonstrate the processes involved during the rapid maturation, because they do not occur in our universe today.

By the end of the second day, God had formed the expanse with all the galaxies and began forming all their celestial spheres. He constructed the internal composition and structure of the proto-stars, proto-planets including Earth, and all the spherical moons. The CMA clearly indicates that God took a special interest in the particular planet-sized sphere called Earth. On this planet, he followed his predetermined plan to produce a habitat suitable for mankind.

Earth has been found by scientists to be a privileged planet in the universe.[10] It was located in a special solar system at a perfect distance from the sun to support life. It has a large single moon that is located at a perfect distance to provide the reflected light of the sun at night and to control tides with their benefits. The star that Earth orbits is located at a very safe distance from the remaining black hole in the dangerous center of the Milky Way galaxy.

Earth had formed with all the naturally occurring atomic elements in what could be unique proportions. So far, no other planet has been found with the same mass and located the same distance from a star like the sun. No stellar systems have been found where the star and a planet's moon can duplicate Earth's gravitational environment. This environment would have affected its formation and its function as an optimum human habitat.

Note that while these processes were occurring to form the proto-planet that became Earth, similar processes were occurring throughout the universe. Proto-stars were formed from the largest spheres of atomic matter and remained mainly in gaseous form. Proto-planets of various types were formed from the mid-sized spheres and were surrounded by moons that were formed into the smallest spheres. Each sphere has a unique mixture of atomic elements largely dependent on their size and location. They are all located where God placed them in their stellar system and galaxy.

The distribution of the galaxies in the large-scale structure of the universe was another sign of the glory and power of the Creator God. Even astronomers who support evolution have to acknowledge the design found in the heavens. Halton Arp writes, "The two clusters [of galaxies] are such a good match in all details, including the hierarchy of intrinsic red shifts, that I am tempted to say that if there is a creator we might expect to hear: 'Look you dummies, I showed you the Virgo Cluster and you did not believe it so I will show you another one just like it and if you still don't believe it—well let's forget the whole thing.'"[11] The signs of the Creator have been observed everywhere in his creation. It just takes some humans longer than others to recognize them for what they are.

The large-scale structure of the universe was completed, and the foundations of the stars, planets, and moons, were established on the second day. They matured rapidly so that the whole universe was then prepared for the divine actions of the Creator and Maker that were to follow.

CHAPTER 5

Divine Action 4: Preparing Planet Earth's Surface

DAY 3A: GATHERING WATERS, MAKING DRY LAND APPEAR

THE PREVIOUS THREE chapters described God's actions or miracles that created and formed our universe on a cosmic scale. This universe, as modeled at the end of the second day, consisted of a large 4-D space-time filled with a web-like fabric made of clumps of atomic matter separated by nearly empty space and held together by gravitational force fields. The clumps of matter were separated into proto-galaxies that consisted of large numbers of proto-stars, proto-planets, and proto-moons. The prefix *proto-* is used in front of a word to describe an unfinished item that requires further transformation to become part of the finished creation.

All the celestial spheres were made of atomic matter that consisted of many different mixtures of the same chemical elements and their compounds as can be found on Earth. Only the proportions of the various chemical elements differed according to the spherical body's size, its location, and its ultimate purpose. By the end of the second day, all these spheres of atomic matter had cooled to a low enough temperature that, at most, they emitted only a small amount of visible light. The foundations of the celestial spheres were taking form. Nighttime returned to the universe and especially to the surface of the proto-planet that would become Earth.

At this point in its report, the author of the CMA changes the perspective away from the cosmic heavens to focus on this single proto-planet. In Genesis 1:9 the author of the CMA reported God's actions at the beginning (evening) of the third day. Specifically, the actions God used to prepare the surface of this planet for animal and human habitation is described. According to the CM-model, the planet had formed from very hot plasma into a spherical globe of mixed chemical compounds in a molten liquid form called magma. The mixture of compounds that formed the top layer of magma first cooled and then separated into the form of all the gases, liquids, and solids that are still found abundantly throughout the crust of the planet. The magma of the outer crust had solidified around chambers filled with liquids and gases and rested on top of the molten magma of the mantle as shown in Illustration 5.1. This crust formed the foundation for the surface of the whole planet.

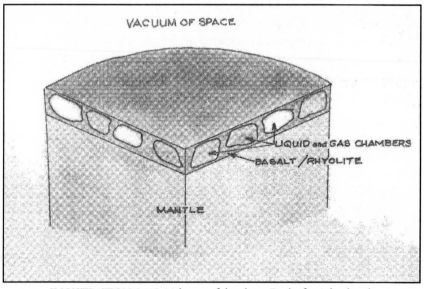

ILLUSTRATION 5.1: Initial crust of the planet Earth after it hardened.

According to the CMA, God first commanded seawater to gather in one place. On a newly formed spherical planet, only the surface can be called a place where water could gather. Logically, an atmosphere must have formed at the same time to protect the surface water from the near vacuum and ultra-cold of outer space. As a result, at one point in the nighttime of the third day, seas first covered the whole surface of the planet and the atmosphere covered the seas. The original atmosphere had formed from gases released out of the same or other chambers like those where the seawater formed within Earth's crust. These actions had to take place at supernatural rates to be completed in far less than a half day.

Then God continued his surface-forming miracle by commanding at least one landmass to rise out of the still molten mantle, pass through fissures in the hardened crust, and build up to appear above sea level. As another result of that command, the seawater retreated to its newly formed basins made by the land rising above and spreading on the surface of the crust. The granite foundations of at least one continent were then established on top of the crust, which still retained many underground seawater and atmospheric gas reservoirs.

As the heated seawater ran off the raised land it picked up a large amount of broken-up and eroded rock and deposited it along its route and in the ocean basins as sediment. At the upper ends of the valleys on dry land, springs of fresh water formed and provided the water for rivers and lakes.

It is apparent from the CMA (v. 13) that the atmosphere did not remain a dark cloud that normally forms from volcanoes. It had to be transformed on the third day into its final habitable mixture from its original composition. The original composition most likely consisted of a mixture of gases and dust that would not support life. We speculate that this transformation was accomplished by burning of the original chemical elements and compounds in the atmosphere. This burning in the atmosphere may have provided the light for the daylight period on the third day and also chemical fertilizer for the topsoil.

A second source, cosmic in nature, for the visible light on the third day is also proposed in the CM-model. This source was provided by the second white hole at the center of the galaxy rotating so that its output was directed toward Earth for half a day. It would have rotated around while forming a second arm of the spiral Milky Way galaxy that is closer to the center. The light source could have been the combination of direct visible light and an aurora effect caused by Earth's newly formed magnetic field and atmosphere around the planet, catching high-energy cosmic ray particles from the same white hole.

Both of the proposed sources of light for the third day would have been one-time events that required God's control of processes and their rates in the physical universe. All the events that provided the surface habitat of Earth with its seas and dry land protected by a perfect atmosphere took place in less than a day and would have been a miracle because they had occurred at supernatural rates. This was another example of the rapid maturing processes taking place during the week of creation. The resulting environment on the surface of the planet provided a perfect habitat for plants later on this day and the creatures that would live there two days later. Only the Creator and Maker of the universe could have accomplished so much in such a short time.

OTHER BIBLICAL REFERENCES TO MIRACLE 4

Psalm 104:6–9

You covered it with the deep as with a garment; the waters were standing above the mountains. At Your rebuke they fled, at the sound of Your thunder they hurried away. The mountains rose; the valleys sank down to the place which You established for them. You set a boundary that they may not pass over, so that they will not return to cover the earth.
—Ps. 104:6–9

We described Psalm 104 in a previous chapter as a hymn of praise to God for his miraculous works in making this world. The verses above continued the series of allusions the author provided to God's miraculous actions during creation week. In verses 2b–4 the author had described some of God's actions in separating the created fluid blob (waters) and making the expanse of the heavens on the second day. The author of the CMA reported the final result of those actions as the separation of "waters below" from "waters above" (Gen. 1:7). This action established the foundations of the planet called Earth: its core, mantle, and crust. Geologists have found that the planet contained a combination solid and molten metal core, surrounded by a shell of molten mantle rock and encased in a shell of solid crust.

The Earth is pictured in verse 6 of this psalm with a deep ocean covering its whole surface as a garment. According to the CMA timeline, that ocean would have resulted from God's first command on the third day when he said, "Let the waters below the heavens be gathered into one place" (Gen. 1:9a). The one place where water could have gathered was the surface of the newborn planet.

Verses 7 and 8 of Psalm 104 describe the seawater receding from covering the land because of another of God's commands. According to verse 8 of the NASB translation, God formed pathways and basins for the seawater by raising mountains and lowering valleys. An alternative translation is given in the King James Version. There we read in verse 8: "They go up by the mountains; they go down by the valleys unto the place which thou hast founded for them." In this version, the subject "they" refers to the rebuked waters of verses 6–7. Because water flows only downhill, the average height of the landmass must have risen above sea level in at least one area of the surface of the planet. This would have resulted from God's second command on the third day when he said, "Let the dry land appear" (Gen 1:9b).

In verse 9, shorelines of the risen landmass were pictured as providing boundaries to the newborn seas as also reported in Jeremiah 5:22. God set these boundaries so that the seawater did not return immediately to cover the land. Together these verses of the psalm pictured events occurring in rapid succession as required by the timeline of the CMA. The author of the CMA reported that these events took place in less time than a full day.

Job 38:4–11

> *Where were you when I laid the foundation of the earth? Tell Me, if you have understanding, who set its measurements? Since you know. Or who stretched the line on it? On what were its bases sunk? Or who laid its cornerstone, when the morning stars sang together and all the sons of God shouted for joy? Or who enclosed the sea with doors when, bursting forth, it went out from the womb; when I made a cloud its garment and thick darkness its swaddling band, and I placed boundaries on it and set a bolt and doors, and I said, "Thus far you shall come, but no farther; and here shall your proud waves stop"?*
>
> —Job 38:4–11

To set the context for these verses, God directed rhetorical questions to Job (and through him, to all mankind) about his actions at some point in the history of the world. The question in verse 4 is about God's action of laying the foundation of the Earth's surface. Laying a foundation, determining its measurements (v. 5), sinking its bases, and laying its cornerstone (v. 6) are all the acts performed by a builder when he begins to construct a building. The foundations of the surface were constructed only once by God on the third day as part of his preparations of Earth's surface for the physical habitat of mankind.

The obvious answer to the "who" questions in these verses is given in verses 9–11, since it was God speaking to Job (Job 38:1). The other questions required Job to remember what he had been taught about God making the world and possibly to encourage him to do research in order to determine how it was done. Any research, if done properly, would have provided Job with answers that are consistent with what was reported in the CMA and any other references to God's actions during the creating-and-making week.

The relevant information for the CM-model provided by these verses is what God did to form the surface into a habitat for living creatures. When God established Earth's foundations, it included both determining the dimensions and boundaries of the dry land and sea. This description of God's action in setting the foundations of Earth's surface complements the CMA report. God laid the foundations (the planet) before he commanded first the waters to gather and then the dry ground to appear.

According to the most popular interpretation of verse 7, it may indicate that these events took place in front of heavenly witnesses—both physical and spiritual hosts of the heavens. The *morning stars* could have referred to the proto-stars that, according to the CM-model, had been formed the previous day. They were not made into lights or actual stars until the following day. The phrase *sons of God* may be Job's way of referring to God's angels. The angels apparently had been created earlier, as they had already played a role controlling winds and flames of fire in the making of the expanse and its hosts (Ps. 104:4, in light of Heb. 1:7). In this verse, perhaps both types of heavenly hosts responded with a joyful noise in witnessing the divine actions God performed on our planet. This would have been consistent with one of the purposes for which both spiritual and physical hosts of heavens were created—to praise the Creator God (Ps. 148:1–6).

God's second question, beginning in verse 8, provides more details of what he did on the third day. First, it alludes to the final result of this divine action: the dry land as the fixed boundaries of the seas. But before that, the seawater had come "bursting forth" out of its "womb" or place of birth. This pictures the crust of the Earth as the source with reservoirs in it as the places where the seawater formed.

In verse 9 the author hints that God formed an initial atmosphere at the same time as the seas. It is pictured in the form of a "cloud" of "thick darkness" as a "swaddling band" over the seas. In Biblical times a swaddling band was the cloth that mothers used to wrap their newborn babies. We infer that both the seawater and the gases for the atmosphere originated from within the crust of the Earth. After bursting forth, the seawater gathered to cover the whole surface of the planet with the atmosphere forming above it.

The next two verses indicate that God set boundaries on the sea like a bolted door so that the waters would stay off the dry land. The final result was dry land surrounded by the seas, or alternatively, seas surrounded by dry land, but mainly that the shores effectively held back the seawater. The author of the CMA reported this same event as God commanding the dry land to appear. In Psalm 136:6 we read: "To him who spread out the earth above the waters."

In verse 11, God told Job he had commanded the waves to stop at the seashores. It can be inferred that this is the same command reported in Jeremiah 5:22 that resulted in setting the boundaries of the seas: "For I have placed the sand as a boundary for the sea, an eternal decree, so it cannot cross over it. Though the waves toss, yet they cannot prevail; though they roar, yet they cannot cross over it." This command is also alluded to in Psalm 104:9 and Proverbs 8:29.

Proverbs 8:24–30

When there were no depths I was brought forth, when there were no springs abounding with water. Before the mountains were settled, before the hills I was brought forth; while He had not yet made the earth and fields, nor the first dust of the world. When He established the heavens, I was there, when He inscribed a circle on the face of the deep, when He made firm the skies above, when the springs of the deep became fixed, when He set for the sea its boundary so that the water would not transgress His command, when He marked out the foundations of the earth; then I was beside Him, as a master workman; and I was daily His delight, rejoicing always before Him.

—Prov. 8:24–30

In verses 24–26, wisdom reported that she was present at a time before the oceans and dry land were established on the third day. It can be inferred the "He" of verse 26 referred to the Creator as reported in the CMA.

Wisdom reported next that the Creator first established the heavens and then the oceans and skies that covered the surface of the planet (vv. 27–28). The Hebrew word translated *skies* in verse 28 is not the same word used for *heavens* in verse 27. In some translations the word *clouds* is used (e.g. KJV, NIV). It is reasonable to assume that verse 28 refers to the birth of seas and atmosphere as reported in Job 38:8–9. The Hebrew word translated *circle* is the only word in that language which could refer to a spherical object or globe. In the context of this verse, it may refer to the global surface of the Earth. (It is used in a similar context in Isaiah 40:22.)

And wisdom finishes her report of events with the setting of the boundaries to the seas by the establishment of at least one dry landmass (v. 29). The only time in the history of Earth when all these events could have taken place was during the third day of creation and making. In the last verse, wisdom reports her role as a skilled builder participating in these divine acts of God and rejoicing in the results.

More General References

In the two clauses of Genesis 1:9, God commanded the seawater to gather in one place and the dry land to appear. Other references to the results caused by these two commands can be identified because they followed the end of the second day and the making of the expanse. The major events of the second day were the stretching out of the heavens and construction of the celestial bodies from the separated "waters."

In addition to the more detailed descriptions in Psalm 104, Job 38, and Proverbs 8, other references to the seawater being gathered and poured out to cover the surface of the whole planet are Psalm 24:1–2, 33:7–9, 95:4–5, 136:6; Amos 5:8, 9:6; and 2 Peter 3:5. There are also numerous references to the establishment of the foundations of the dry land so that it appeared above sea level: 1 Samuel 2:8; Psalm 89:11, 102:25, 119:90–91, 136:6; Proverbs 3:19; Isaiah 48:13, 51:13, 51:16; Jeremiah 5:22, 10:12, 33:2, 51:15; Zechariah 12:1; and Hebrews 1:10. All these reports are complementary to the words of the CMA, and they describe the resulting products of God's fourth divine action on the third day.

Scientific Terminology

Seawater

Water found in the oceans and seas is definitely not pure molecular water (H_2O). Scientists have found it contains most of the same minerals and chemical compounds that are found in dry ground. These minerals are found in the form of salts and other dissolved and suspended solid compounds. Even the purest spring water contains some of these same minerals. We speculate that water that gathered on the surface of the planet came from a place where all these other minerals were also present. That place of origin would have been within the crust of the planet.

Atmosphere

The atmosphere was formed by gases surrounding the planet. Air is a mixture of many gaseous elements and compounds. The four gases that are found in greatest proportions in the atmosphere are nitrogen, oxygen, carbon dioxide, and water vapor. These gases could have formed within the crust of the planet just like the seawater. Most of the rocks in the crust contain one or more of the chemical elements that formed these gases. Many of these same gases are still being vented from underground chambers in geysers and volcanic eruptions.

Earth's Surface

A spherical planet has only one location that can be identified as a single place where a liquid such as seawater could gather—its surface. With enough seawater, the whole surface of the planet would have been covered. There is currently enough water in the oceans to cover the whole surface to an average depth of 2.4 km (1.5 miles), if the surface of the crust were smooth.

Molten Pluton

A molten pluton consists of a mixture of melted chemical compounds that form solid rock as it cools. The molten rock is called magma when it is underground and lava when it flows from a volcano. The pluton is formed within the solid crust of the Earth by magma as it pushes up from below the crust into fissures and cavities. When a pluton breaks through the crust, the liquid rock solidifies rapidly and forms extrusive igneous rocks with microscopic-size crystals such as rhyolite and basalt. When kept under specific temperature and pressure conditions within the crust as it cooled, the magma in the pluton would form the larger crystals of an intrusive igneous rock such as granite.

Dry Ground

Geologists have identified three types of rocks that formed the dry ground on Earth. The majority of rocks were igneous, and they extended down through the crust and into the mantle of the planet. They were formed when their chemical compounds were mixed and crystallized from molten liquid magma as it cooled. Examples of igneous rocks are granite, basalt, and rhyolite. These igneous rocks formed the foundation rock strata that cover the Earth's multi-phased mantle. They were pushed up well above sea level to form some of the mountains on any landmass.

A second type of rock is the sedimentary rock. The majority of this type of rock resulted from a mixture of pre-existing pieces of rock and a cementing compound that settled out of a body of water due to gravity. The application of heat and pressure by various natural processes to the sediment resulted in the formation of the sedimentary rock strata. One major sedimentary rock-forming process is called lithification, where heat and pressure from surrounding rock compact and harden the sediment mixture. Examples of sedimentary rocks formed from mixtures of small grains of rock are limestone, sandstone, and mudstone. Larger pieces of rock cemented together in various mixtures form the clastic or composite sedimentary rocks that look a lot like concrete. Boulders of igneous rock, as large as houses, are found in layers of clastic sedimentary rock.

Researchers have found that the surfaces of the continents are covered with multiple layers of various sedimentary rocks. These multiple layers of sedimentary rock have an average depth of 1.7 km (1 mile) on the continents. But there are sedimentary rock strata that also extend into the oceans near the continents. The only areas on the landmasses that are not covered with sedimentary rock are located where granite or lava formed mountains that were pushed up through the layers of sedimentary rocks. In certain places, the sedimentary rock layers are stacked up to 13 km (8 miles) deep along the border of the continents.

The third type of rock is metamorphic. These rocks are formed when igneous or sedimentary rocks are reheated and their basic physical and chemical structure modified under great pressure. Examples of metamorphic rocks are marble that is formed from calcium carbonate (limestone), quartzite formed from silicon dioxide (sandstone), and gneiss formed from granite. Many metamorphic rock formations are found near regions of mountain building where a granite or basaltic pluton pushed through igneous and/or sedimentary rock strata.

Aurora

Auroras are often observed in both of the polar regions of Earth. They are caused by high-energy particles that are captured in Earth's magnetic field. They give up some of their energy by emitting photons when they attach themselves to ions in the upper atmosphere. The auroras are located in the ionosphere at an altitude of approximately 80 km (50 miles). The major sources of the high-energy particles are the solar wind from the sun and cosmic rays from outside the solar system.

THE CM-MODEL

We developed the CM-model to include the miracles of the second day where God had divided the fluid blob into droplets and separated them with expanses of space. First, black holes were formed, and then they spewed out all the celestial spheres through white holes in their event horizons to form galaxies. These galaxies of celestial spheres are located throughout the universe. By the end of the second day, God had also formed a specific proto-planet. It was located in a star system with seven other major planets. God chose it as the privileged planet, and on the third day began to make it into a habitat for all his living creatures.

This proto-planet cooled to temperatures where it did not emit visible light as the second day ended. We speculated that the heavier metallic elements, such as iron and nickel, sank to the center where they formed a composite core of liquid and solid metals under great pressure. As the liquid and solid cores slowed their rotation at different rates, an electrical current began to flow in the liquid core that generates the magnetic field of the planet. Exactly how this current was initiated has not been determined at this time. According to Humphreys' calculations, the magnetic field from the current loop contained its maximum energy on the third day and has decreased ever since.[1]

In a shell around the core, a mantle of hot liquid and solid silicon-based compounds initially formed a sea of magma that supported a solidifying outer layer called the crust. The crust solidified as a combination of igneous rock and chambers filled with seawater and other liquid or gaseous compounds as shown in Illustration 5.1. It formed the foundation of the Earth's surface.

Divine Act 4

Let the waters under the expanse gather [on the surface] and let dry land appear [above sea level].
—Gen. 1:9, paraphrased

Again, the author of the CMA reported briefly and in very general terms the processes and results for the miracles that took place during the nighttime of the third day. The two miracles reported divided the surface of the planet into oceans and dry land. An atmosphere was also provided to turn this surface into a habitat for living creatures.

Birth of the Oceans and Atmosphere

Following the CMA timeline, we extend the CM-model first with seawater being gathered on the surface of the proto-planet in relative darkness on the evening of the third day. We speculate that the seawater was forced out from the underground chambers within the crust where it had formed as shown in Illustration 5.2. Great pressure was on these chambers of liquid as the crust cooled and solidified around them. At God's command, the top boundaries of the chambers broke up, and the seawater escaped through volcanic and geyser-like action as described in Job 38:8: "bursting forth." Enough seawater burst forth to cover the whole surface as described in Psalm 104:6: "covered . . . as with a garment." At the same time as the seawater poured out, gaseous compounds were being forced out from their reservoirs in the crust, and they formed the initial atmosphere as described in Job 38:9: "When I made a cloud its [the sea's] garment and a thick darkness its swaddling band."

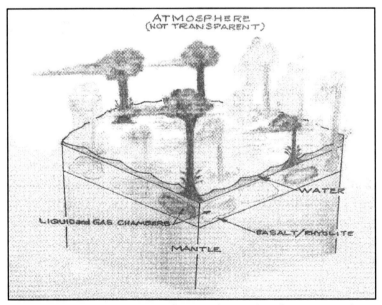

ILLUSTRATION 5.2: Water gathering and atmosphere forming on Earth.

We speculated that the foundation-laying process for the surface of the planet started with the formation of the planet when God had separated its molten fluids from the "waters above" (Gen. 1:7). The second day ended after that separation took place, according to Genesis 1:8. We further speculated that the cooling process that formed the solid crust and laid the foundations continued into the evening of the third day. The surface was first declared complete and perfect after the dry land had appeared above sea level later on the third day (Gen. 1:10). Logically for the model, we infer from this timeline that all the events described in Job 38:4–11 complement the CMA. They took place between the time God formed the planet on the second day and when the dry land had appeared and was established as the boundaries to the seas.

This sequence of events is supported by other references in the Bible to the same events. For example, in both Amos 5:8 and 9:6 the author reports that God "calls for the waters of the sea and pours them out on the surface of the [whole] earth." Psalm 104:6 describes the original ocean as a garment covering the surface and even the highest hills or mountains. According to the implied timing, some hills or mountains existed before the water covered them. The author of Proverbs 8:27–28 reported the establishment of the skies above a deep sea that formed the surface of the globe. It is also reported there that the water in the sea came from deep springs that God had established. These underground sources most likely provided enough water to cover Earth's surface at two different times in recorded history, first during creation week (2 Pet. 3:5b) and then again during the flood in Genesis chapters 6–8 (2 Pet. 3:6).

From scientific data, we infer that the crust of the planet grew thicker as it cooled and became a solid. We speculate that the cooling crust would have built up a tremendous pressure in the chambers of fluids and gases just below its surface by shrinking as a result of the change from fluid magma to solid rock. The pressure would have been released rapidly by venting the contents of the chambers through the surface similar to water squeezed from a sponge. At the same time, the contents would have forced up pieces of the solid crust that had formed the ceilings of the chambers. These most likely became the original hills or mountains. The chemical compounds within the chambers such as seawater, dust, and various gases would have poured out from openings in the crust as gigantic geysers and volcanoes.

For the CM-model, we speculate that this extreme volcanic and geyser-like action was spread out over the entire surface of the planet. The scale of these physical processes must have been immense to explain the volume of water that was required to cover the surface of Earth. Also, a very large volume of gases was required to form Earth's atmosphere. We can obtain a general idea of the enormous scale of this activity from volcanoes and geysers that have erupted recently on Earth. They expelled large amounts of mineralized water and great quantities of various gases, smoke, and dust into the atmosphere. But their output amounted to only a very small percentage (much less than 1 percent) of the oceans or the atmosphere.

In the short timeline of the CMA, all this volcanic and geyser-like action took place immediately at God's command and everywhere on the surface of the planet. The whole process occurred fast enough to leave time for a landmass to appear, the atmosphere transformed to support plant life, and plants to sprout and mature on the dry land before the end of the third day.

We further speculate that some of the large chunks of surface rock that were lifted up were also broken or eroded into smaller pieces by the hot seawater and gases as they flowed to cover the surface. The hot seawater could have rapidly eroded larger chunks of rock into the granules that formed sediment. The water would also have carried a large quantity of this sediment while it was moving very fast to gather on the surface. After the global ocean had reached its maximum level, the motion of the seawater would have slowed down. As it slowed, the water would have deposited the collected rubble into sediment beds of all shapes and sizes. The mixtures of stones, gravel, and sand in these sediments can still be found in most strata of sedimentary rocks.

Making the Land Appear

The second part of God's fourth miracle as reported in the CMA caused at least one landmass to appear above sea level. This is described in Job 38:10 as bolting the doors and locking the sea behind them so the waves will stop on the shores of the dry land. Psalm 104:7–9 provided more detail on the actions that took place to accomplish this. These verses report that God commanded the waters to retreat from a level above the highest hills by causing them to flow to their basins. This took place because at least one continent with mountains and valleys rose above sea level as shown in Illustration 5.3. The mountains and valleys provided paths for the seawater to follow. The seawater ultimately gathered in basins where the continent of land had not formed.

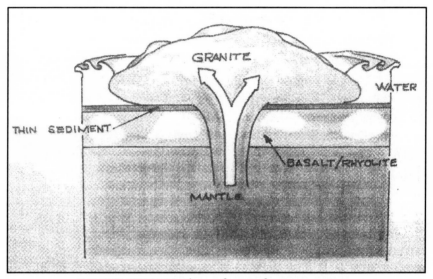

ILLUSTRATION 5.3: Pluton of granite forming a continent.

Then God established the shorelines of the raised landmass as the boundary for the seas so that they prevented the sea from flowing back over the drying land. In Proverbs 8:28, the author adds to this scenario that God also set the output of the deep springs from the chambers that remained in Earth's crust to maintain a balance to the water level in the ocean and that which was required to water the risen land.

Granite Base Formation

Geologists have found a layer of extrusive igneous rock everywhere under both the oceans and continents. Under the oceans, this igneous rock is mainly basalt and rhyolite. Under the continents, the composition of this igneous rock layer cannot easily be determined. The granite rock layer that formed the foundations of the continents was laid on top of it, and this granite layer was very thick and massive. Granite, rhyolite, and basalt formed the majority of the rock strata that are the basement rocks of the continents.

Granite was an intrusively formed igneous rock and differed from basalt in both the mixture of its chemical compounds and the size of its crystals. Rhyolite was the extrusive igneous rock formed from the same chemical mixture as granite but has the smaller crystals similar to basalt. It can be inferred from the larger crystals of granite that it cooled at a slower rate than basalt or rhyolite, so the larger crystals had time to grow. The chemical mixture of lighter elements in both granite and rhyolite make them lighter in weight than the same volume of basalt. We speculate that the slower cooling rate and larger crystals resulted because the granite began to take form while still below the surface of the crust and under the seawater. Once it reached the optimum temperature and crystallization began, it was pushed up through the surface under great pressure where it cooled more rapidly.

The rock in the mantle under the hardening crust would have remained molten magma for a longer period of time because it retained a higher temperature. The molten granite could have formed a pluton in the crust at the beginning of the third day with God's command for the seawater to gather. The crust would have started to break open and weaken with that command. The extreme volcanism and geyser-like action caused by the seawater and gases pouring out may have caused cracks to form in the crust. We speculate that at one point on the globe, a molten granite pluton from the mantle could have pushed up into a large crack in the crust. As the pluton moved up toward the seawater on the surface, it cooled enough to reach the temperature where solidifying and crystallization of the granite rock began. When it reached the surface of the crust, it could have been fluid enough that it spread out over the basaltic crust displacing seawater to form the landmass of a continent. In Proverbs 8:29 the author reports that God directed the formation of the dry landmass and determined its size. Granite became the major component in the foundational rock of the continents. This landmass rested on the basaltic crust, and its surface had risen above sea level.

Scientists have not been able to produce granite artificially or find an active source on Earth that is presently forming it naturally. Granite probably only forms when special conditions of temperature and pressure are applied to a specific mixture of its chemical ingredients. These conditions could have occurred within a molten pluton that began the process of crystallization under precise pressure and temperature conditions while within the crust. If the granite in the pluton had reached the seawater on the surface of the crust too soon, it would have cooled much more rapidly. In that case, instead of the large crystals of granite forming, it would have become the extrusive rhyolite with the smaller microscopic crystals.

The temperature of formation for granite (also its melting temperature) has been found to be dependent upon the amount of water present at the time of crystallization. The crystals that resulted are coarse-grained and tightly interlocking and consist mainly of four silicate compounds. These compounds were quartz, feldspar, mica, and hornblende. Impurities of many types are trapped within the crystals of these compounds. Some of these impurities have retained information on the temperature at the time of crystallization and how long ago that process took place.

We speculate that the landmass covered thousands of square kilometers of surface area. On top of the granite foundation, seawater would have deposited sediment layers. As the granite pushed up through the crust and entered the seawater, the water would have carried some of the sediment away. According to Psalm 104:8, the seawater retreated to its basins passing by mountains and through the valleys when the land rose up. New mountains were most likely formed by granite pushing through the surface sediment on top of the pluton. The seawater could have traveled long distances as it ran off the pluton. As it traveled, the water would have eroded the fresh granite rock into more sediment and carried both the new and old sediment into the ocean basins.

Below the oceans, the broken-open chambers in the crust would have refilled with seawater and sediment. The ceilings and walls of the chambers could have collapsed and formed large depressions in the surface of the crust. These depressions resulted in deep basins for the seawater that ran off the rising continent. We speculate that on a planet-wide scale, the collapsed chambers would have been concentrated where the largest and deepest ocean basins formed.

Metamorphic Rock Formation

Above the basement igneous rock, there are many mixed layers of sedimentary and metamorphic rocks. As described above, metamorphic rock was made from physically modified igneous and sedimentary rocks. This rock was re-crystallized under high temperature and pressure so that it took on a different crystal structure than the original rock from which it formed. For the CM-model, we speculate that this process took place at the same time the granite pluton was rising to its final elevation and location. Heat and pressure from the pluton could have softened and modified the igneous and sedimentary rocks that were close to where the pluton traveled. As the pluton pushed through and rose out of the igneous rock layer of the crust, it could have melted sediment that had been deposited by the seawater on that surface.

The motion of the pluton through the crust could have supplied the added pressure required for melted compounds to be transformed into their modified crystal structure. It has been estimated that a pressure equal to 38 km (23 miles) of rock stacked on top of it was required to make marble from melted limestone. The pressure from the layers of rock presently above where marble is found would not have been enough to cause its formation. For the formation of marble, the combined pressure of the rising pluton and the weight of the rock and seawater above it would have been required.

Sedimentary Rock Strata Formation

Earlier we speculated that a layer of sediment made of rocks, gravel, and soil settled from the water after the original ocean had formed. Like the metamorphic rock, some of this sediment could have been turned into rock when the granite pluton pushed through the crust and made contact with the sediment. This process could have caused lithification of the sediment near the edges and on top of the continent. Where the original sedimentary rock was formed has not been determined. The waters of the Genesis Flood (Gen. 6–8) rearranged the whole surface of the planet and could have relocated a large percentage of the original sedimentary rock strata.

Remaining Crust

The original surface crust of igneous basaltic rock that remained under the oceans and may exist under much of the granite landmass most likely retained some subterranean water reservoirs. Enough water remained in underground reservoirs of the crust so that they were a major source of water for the Genesis Flood (Gen. 7:11). Recent research has revealed that large quantities of water still exist in and even under the crust to this day. Below the crust, geologists have found an estimated five times the amount of water contained in all the oceans.[2]

Out-Gassing as the Source of an Atmosphere

We speculate that all the atmospheres of planets and moons in the solar system were formed from gases that originally formed within those celestial bodies. For the proposed CM-model, the source of those gases was atomic elements already present within the hot fluids of plasma and magma that were ejected from white holes on the second day. Those hot fluids became stars, planets, and moons as they were moved to their present locations in their stellar systems and galaxies. All the atmospheres that have been investigated are on planets and moons of our solar system. They all contain the same atomic elements and similar gaseous compounds only in different proportions and quantities.

On other planets of our solar system and some of their moons, active venting of gaseous compounds into their thin atmospheres has been observed. This venting even occurs into space when they have not established any permanent atmosphere. These planets and moons are the same ones that scientists who support evolution have claimed to be billions of years old.

Like these other planets and moons, scientific research has found that Earth has continued to vent gases into its oceans and atmosphere. The Earth had several advantages over the other planets and moons when God established its atmosphere to support plant life and all the living creatures. It had more water and other critical atmospheric gases trapped in its crust than found so far on any other planet or moon. Earth also was located at a distance from the sun where it could maintain a more moderate temperature than the other planets. It also has a gravitational field and a magnetic field that were optimum for retaining the required gases once they were released to form the atmosphere.

Evolutionary Model and the Source of Earth's Atmosphere

One popular evolutionary model put forth to explain the origin of terrestrial planets and solar system moons involved their formation from solids, liquids, and gases by accumulation. They accumulated material from collisions with other objects in a disc of material remaining around the early sun.[3] The materials in the disk were the remains left behind when the sun supposedly formed from a cloud of molecular gases. How solid material remained in the disk rather than collapsing into the sun is not explained. But these evolutionists claim that over a long time period, multiple collisions of smaller clumps of rock material continued until the planet or moon grew to its final size.

This model of a planet or moon formation has run into some major difficulties. One difficulty is how all the clumps of matter were first attracted and held together when their gravity was not strong enough. Another difficulty was how to explain the results of the collisions that would have been required. The result of a random process like collisions cannot be predicted or modeled without unverifiable assumptions. The amount of material added and subtracted at each collision cannot be calculated from theory without knowing the weight and speed of the objects colliding. Most of the conditions used in the models are based on assumptions about the objects that the modelers just choose but cannot verify. This constitutes a case of circular reasoning and choosing the appropriate starting conditions could produce any result that was desired.

The source of the gases that formed a planet's atmosphere would be especially difficult for this evolutionary model to demonstrate. All the gases that formed from the colliding clumps of rocks would have escaped into space until the proto-planet had reached sufficient size and density for its gravity to hold onto these hot gases. In other words, smaller proto-planets would have lost all their gaseous products during multiple collisions. So by the time the planet grew large enough to retain gases, they would have already escaped into space in previous collisions.

These evolutionary scientists have proposed an implausible explanation for the source of atmospheric gases. They proposed that one or more comets bearing the required amount of the gases for a planet's atmosphere must have struck the planet once it was of sufficient size. However, they have not been successful in explaining the unlikely timing for such an event or the source of those comets. Another problem with this explanation was that comets with the correct proportions of the gaseous elements required have yet to be found in the solar system.

Astronomers have more closely studied atmospheres on three of the four terrestrial planets and one frozen moon in the solar system. The hot gas giants and outer frozen planets are thought to have formed from the same gaseous compounds that formed the sun. Most of the moons in the solar system have only small transient atmospheres or none at all. Of the three terrestrial planets with measurable atmospheres, only Earth has a predominantly nitrogen atmosphere. Atmospheres on Venus and Mars consist mainly of carbon dioxide. The only moon in the solar system with a permanent atmosphere is Saturn's moon Titan, and it has a predominantly nitrogen atmosphere similar to the Earth. These facts about the other atmospheres in the solar system demonstrate that each is a unique result of the original conditions on the planet or moon on which they are found. Out-gassing is the best explanation for the source of an atmosphere, but it is not reasonable in the 4-billion-year time frame of an evolutionary model. All the gases within the planet or moon would have been expended in a much shorter time period.

Dawn of Day 3

The author of the CMA reported that the third day was a normal day with a period of nighttime and a period of daylight (Gen 1:13). The events described above could all have taken place during the night. Neither the CMA nor any other Bible verse reported what the physical source of visible light was for the second half of the third day. To be called daylight, this light had to at least visibly illuminate the surface of Earth that existed at that time. We infer from the likely sources of light on previous days that God used a physical process that he had previously made to produce this light. There are at least two options for natural processes that existed on the third day for a source of visible light that would fit the CMA and the conditions within the CM-model as developed up to this point. The two options are a cosmic source and an atmospheric source. Because the cosmic source also depends on a transparent atmosphere, both are included in the CM-model.

Cosmic Source for Daylight

The cosmic source is related to the formation of the Milky Way galaxy. As explained in the previous chapter, the CM-model was based on reasonable speculation that a spiral galaxy like the Milky Way was formed by two white holes on opposite sides of a rotating ultra-massive black hole. The white holes produced EMR and jets of atomic matter that formed the celestial bodies in the arms of the spiral pattern as they rotated about the center of the galaxy. The most recent observations by astronomers have revealed that the Milky Way galaxy presently appears with a bar at the center where the two major spiral arms extend out from opposite ends (Illustration 4.4). We also speculated that the ends of the bar may now be quasars pointed away from Earth.

From the spiral pattern formed by the two main arms, we infer that each end of the bar rotated nearly one full revolution of 360 degrees during the galaxy formation process that began at dawn of the second day and ended on the fourth day. We speculated that the material that became the solar system exited a white hole from one end of the bar during the daylight period of the second day. That white hole could have provided the visible light for the solar system for a period of twelve hours on that day. We further speculate that the jet of EMR and atomic matter from the white hole on the other end of the bar would have rotated into a position where it was directed toward the solar system at the dawn of the third day as shown in Illustration 5.4. The above description assumes the galaxy-forming rotation continued during the third day and God stopped the jets and any rotation of the bar only after the galaxy was completed on the fourth day.

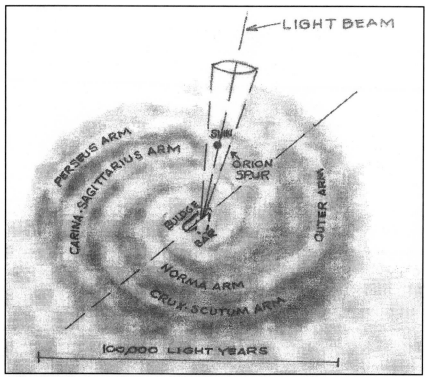

ILLUSTRATION 5.4: Illumination of the Earth by a white hole at the center of the Galaxy.

God could have timed the relative rotation rates of the bar and the proto-stars so that the second white hole provided light on Earth starting at dawn and ending with the evening of the fourth day twelve hours later. During that time, the white hole would have rotated past the position of the solar system, continuing to eject the celestial bodies that formed the remainder of its second arm of the spiral. The rotation may have slowed down to extend the time Earth was illuminated, since the end of the bar rotated only a few degrees past to where it is positioned today.

For these events to have taken place as described, the bar at the center of the galaxy rotated faster than the celestial spheres in the spiral arms during the formation of the galaxy. God could have matched the bar-rotation rate to the remainder of the galaxy once the spiral arms were completed. This would have occurred on the fourth day (Gen. 1:17) when all the stars were set in their relative positions in the galaxy and had started providing their light.

Some assumptions are required for the white hole to be able to supply visible light for the period of daylight on the Earth. We speculate that it would have to supply light to the entire surface. The direct beam from the white hole could only supply light to half of the planet. For the other half of the planet light could have been supplied by a bright aurora that surrounded the planet. This aurora would have formed when cosmic rays from the white hole impinged on the newly formed atmosphere and magnetic field of the planet. On the third day the sun was not yet functioning as a star, so the solar wind had not formed the heliosphere around the sun that now shields the solar system from a significant amount of these external cosmic rays.

One of the main assumptions we are making is that both light and high-energy particles in the form of cosmic rays are traveling at much higher speeds than presently measured on Earth. They would have traveled almost 25,000 light years in much less than a day during the formation of the galaxy. Chapter 7 of this book gives more details on the speed of light during creation week in connection with God completing the stars on the fourth day. Another assumption is that the light emitted by the white hole is over a million times brighter than the light from any recently measured quasar. This would be reasonable if a quasar is only a reduced remnant of a once-active white hole. The third assumption is that the light and cosmic rays emitted by the white hole are in a wide beam that would take twelve hours to pass over Earth. These are all reasonable assumptions only if God is controlling the galaxy formation process. And they demonstrate God's rapid maturing of the galaxy and solar system beyond Earth.

Atmospheric Source Option

The atmospheric source of light for the third day could have resulted from the burning of the original mixture of gases and dust particles in the atmosphere. As reported in Job 38:9, the initial atmosphere was a very thick, dark cloud that caused darkness over the newly born seas. This description pictured the original atmosphere as a cloud composed of gases and solid particles much like the thick dark smoke and dust billowing from erupting volcanoes.

The atmospheres found on some of the other solar planets still retain this characteristic of thick clouds obscuring their surface. Those extraterrestrial atmospheres are made up of compounds of carbon, sulfur, nitrogen, and hydrogen, with only a small amount of oxygen. When these solid and gaseous compounds are mixed with generous amounts of oxygen and hydrogen as found on Earth, they could form an atmosphere that would be highly flammable. Hot lava from volcanoes or even electrical discharges within such an atmosphere could have supplied the ignition sparks for it to begin to burn.

The burning of the solids and gases in the atmosphere would have served two purposes for the CM-model. First, it could have provided visible light for the daylight period of the third day. The burning process would be modeled as starting near the surface and proceeding to higher altitudes as it exhausted the fuel at lower altitudes all around the globe. We speculate that the main products of the burning were gaseous compounds such as carbon dioxide and water vapor that would be heavier than the fuel gases such as hydrogen and hydrocarbons. These gaseous products would have mixed with the nitrogen and oxygen to form a transparent atmosphere.

The second purpose for the burning was the transformation of the non-transparent atmosphere into one that transmitted visible light from the auroras and white hole for the cosmic source to provide the daylight on the third day. This clearing of the air would have been necessary to provide the clear days for the final perfect habitat of plants, animals, and mankind. The formation of carbon dioxide and carbon monoxide from burning carbon particles in oxygen would have removed a black substance from the air and replaced it with two transparent gases. The gaseous products formed from burning hydrocarbons such as methane in oxygen are water vapor, carbon dioxide, and carbon monoxide, all of which are transparent.

Other compounds that were the products of burning such a chemical-rich atmospheric mixture would have been solids such as nitrates, carbonates, and sulfates. These products would have been much heavier than the gases and could have been removed from the atmosphere by gravity. They would have settled rapidly to the surface, forming a layer of these compounds. An additional mixing process could have introduced the compounds into the soil where they would serve as fertilizer. These mineral compounds would have been beneficial in the preparation of the soil for plant life.

With God's guidance, the new atmosphere would have consisted of the perfect mixture of gases required by both plant life and all living creatures. It could have started a greenhouse effect that helped maintain a moderate temperature for the entire surface of the planet. The atmosphere transmitting the higher-energy visible photons from the sun (starting on day four) and absorbing the lower-energy infrared photons that were emitted by the surface of the planet would have caused the greenhouse effect.

Several More Surface Preparation Details

We infer that sufficient sediment remained on the surface of the continent after the seawater runoff to form a layer of soil. How much sediment remained cannot be determined. The layer of soil found on the surface today may not be representative of the original conditions of the surface on the third day because it resulted from the Genesis Flood. We speculate that for the CM-model, the original layer of soil was thick and uniformly distributed enough so that grasses and trees could carpet the whole surface of the continent as reported in Genesis 1:12.

In Genesis 2, the author provided another report on the surface conditions resulting from God's fourth action on the third day. In verse 5, he provided a description of the barren land without trees or any other plants. The author also reported that rain had not yet fallen on the land. In verse 6, it is reported that spring-fed streams watered the whole land surface. We infer that the hydrology cycle as it occurs in nature today started sometime after the sixth day. Rain wasn't reported in the Bible until the Genesis Flood. But the habitat that God had designed and built on the surface of Earth was watered without it.

Also, the soil had been prepared for all kinds of vegetation to sprout and grow on the third day (Gen. 1:11). Without man, only God and his angels could have prepared the soil. The habitat that resulted from miracle 4 was fully functional and it was prepared for the introduction of plant life.

In Psalm 104, the author alludes to the preparation of the surface habitat of the land and the atmosphere for animals and mankind after the seawater runoff was completed. In verse 10, the author reported that God caused freshwater springs to appear that provided water for streams in the valleys. He also caused the moisture in the atmosphere at higher altitudes to condense into water in the form of dew for the surface areas at or near the tops of the mountains (v. 13). In verse 18, it is reported that God had formed the cliffs of rock in which mountain-dwelling animals lived after they were created. We infer from this description that mountains of granite and limestone had been pushed up to form these cliffs.

SCIENTIFIC EVIDENCE THAT SUPPORTS THE CM-MODEL

Three areas of scientific research have produced evidence that supports this portion of the CM-model. The supporting evidence came from research in various sciences associated with geology. The first source of evidence was research on the chemical composition of seawater and the rocks formed from its sediment. The evidence showed that the original ocean was too hot to support life as it is known today. The ratio of two isotopes of oxygen in silicon dioxide (microscopic quartz crystals) provides a direct measurement of the temperature of the water in which this compound crystallized.

The second source was the study of crystals found in granite. This evidence was produced by several different measurements of chemical elements in zircon crystals that are found abundantly in most granite rocks. These crystals are made of zirconium silicate ($ZrSiO_4$). Zircons contain the same two oxygen isotopes as quartz and their ratio also provides information on the temperature of the granite when zircons crystallized. The same technique as with quartz crystals is used. But zircons also contain impurities such as hafnium and helium that provide information on the composition of the magma from which they formed and how long they have been crystallized.

The third source was research on sources of atmospheric gases on planets and moons. This evidence was found by comparing atmospheric conditions on Earth with those on other planets and moons in the solar system. Saturn's moon Titan has been observed still producing atmospheric gases to replace the ones it loses to space. This evidence showed that out-gassing from within the moon was the most probable source of its continuing atmosphere. We speculated above that a similar process formed the atmosphere of Earth.

High Temperature Oceans at the Beginning

The oceans were modeled as formed from high-temperature seawater pouring out from a cooling crust. The silicon dioxide or quartz crystals formed in this water would have formed at higher temperatures than those formed in the oceans today. The crystals of submicroscopic quartz smaller than in common sand are found in the sedimentary rock called chert. Chert was formed by lithification of ocean sediment into rock containing these tiny crystals. Chert has been found in Precambrian rock layers that have been dated as the first sedimentary rock formed under the oceans. Precambrian rock layers are found at the bottom of the sedimentary rock strata, and they contain no evidence of marine life in the form of fossils. The temperature of crystallization of quartz found in the chert showed that the seawater was at a temperature that would not have supported marine life.

Both the atomic elements silicon and oxygen found in the quartz crystals in chert have two stable atomic isotopes. The ratio of the amounts of the two isotopes of either oxygen or silicon in chert has been found to be directly related to the temperature at which the quartz crystals formed in seawater. The measurements of both silicon and oxygen isotope ratios in chert resulted in the same temperature of crystallization. This is considered strong evidence that the chert formed in seawater at or above that temperature. As the author of a recent article on this topic stated, "Both records suggest that average ocean temperatures were between 60°C and 80°C for much of the time between 3.5 billion and 2.0 billion years ago."[4] Measurements of quartz crystals found in recent sediments showed that they crystallized at 20°C or the average temperature of seawater in the oceans today.

The ages for when the crystals formed that were reported in that referenced article are based on assumptions that geological evolution took place. Those assumptions have never been verified. The authors also did not attempt to explain how the oceans would have remained in that temperature range for 1.5 billion years. If process rates were accelerated by God's use of miracles during the week of creating and making and rapid maturing took place as we speculated, those assumptions are definitely wrong. For more information on problems with evolutionary time scales and dating of the rocks, the reader is referred to Don DeYoung's book *Thousands . . . Not Billions.*[5]

Granite Formation and Zircons Tell Tales

As stated previously, the process for forming granite has not been duplicated in any laboratory. Geologists have only speculated on the conditions under which it was formed. Indirect evidence has shown that it formed rapidly and at one time. From the amount of granite contained in the foundations of the continents, we infer that when it formed, the correct combination of molten magma chemical composition, temperature, and pressure was present at a single point in time. No evidence has been found that granite is presently forming anywhere on the planet or that it took millions or billions of years originally to form.

Three Types of Granite Formed at One Time

Geologists have in the past categorized granite rocks into three types. They identified the type by the chemical elements that the sample contained. The M-type (*M* for mantle) contained many of the same elements as basalt that originate in magma from the upper mantle. The S-type (*S* for sediment) contained many of the same elements contained in the sedimentary rock layers that formed on top of the basaltic crust. From the most recent research on the I-type (*I* for igneous) granite rocks, geologists reported that it contains a mixture of the elements found in both the M-type and S-type. The proportions of elements in the mixture of these two types were directly related to the depth where the samples were found in their rock formation.[6]

The measurement of the amount of the hafnium impurity in a zircon crystal within granite was used to determine whether it was crystallized from mantle magma (high hafnium content) or melted sedimentary magma (low hafnium content). Hafnium is a very large and heavy atom with an atomic number of 72 and atomic weight of 178. Once hafnium is trapped in a zircon crystal, it is too large to move about in the crystal. Its large weight would have caused it to be more concentrated near the bottom of a magma pluton. The data showed that the hafnium concentration in zircon crystals of I-type granite increased the deeper the sample was taken in the granite rock formation. These results indicated that the three types of granite are closely related. The I-type is situated between the other two types and represents crystallization of magma from a mixture of both the upper mantle and the melting of sedimentary rocks from the outer layers of the crust.

We infer that this is indirect evidence that molten magma in a pluton crystallized into all three types of granite as it formed a continent. As one author referring to the research stated, "Kemp et al. show that the oxygen and hafnium isotope compositions of zircons in Lachlan I-type granites correlate with one another over a wide range, from compositions characteristic of mantle to those characteristic of upper-crustal sediments. These trends suggest that I-type granites form by mixing of differentiated mantle melts with melts of the upper crust."[7]

Geologists who support evolution have found it difficult to explain how the zircon crystallization process could have taken place over millions of years. Crystallization of magma has to be considered a rapid process much like ice forming in freezing water. Once the critical temperature and pressure was reached, the crystallization took place rapidly. The only reasonable conclusion was that the process of continent building had been completed in a short period of time. According to the CMA, God formed at least one continent on the third day, most likely with a miracle that accelerated the natural process rates involved in its formation.

Water Was Present During Granite Formation

Measurements of the quantities of the two isotopes of oxygen in zircons have revealed that they crystallized in wet conditions. Researchers first determined the temperature of formation of these crystals from the ratio of the quantities of the two oxygen isotopes. This temperature indicated that the granite crystallized near 700°C.[8] A dry zircon grown in a laboratory has been found to melt at a temperature close to 900°C. The presence of water was the only known condition found that could explain the 200°C lower crystallization temperature of the zircons found in granite.

The Age of Zircons

In other research, the amount of helium that remains trapped in these crystals has determined an upper bound to the age of the zircons. Unlike hafnium, helium is a small and lightweight atomic element with atomic number of 2. Helium atoms do not form chemical bonds with other atoms and are found to move freely in a zircon crystal by a process called gas diffusion. The amount of helium retained by zircon crystals limits the time since the zircons formed. The helium gas diffusion rate or out-gassing from zircons was found to be too large to support millions of years of existence for the zircons. From research conducted recently on zircons, creation-supporting scientists reported that the amount of helium in zircon crystals would support an age of thousands of years but not the billions of years required for the evolutionary models of Earth formation.[9]

Titan's Source for an Atmosphere

Titan is a moon of the ringed planet Saturn. The atmosphere of Titan was measured by instruments on a satellite placed in orbit around Saturn during recent flybys and also by similar instruments in a small landing module. From these sources scientists have found that Titan's upper atmosphere is composed of 97 percent nitrogen, 2.2 percent methane, and 0.4 percent hydrogen. They could not explain how Titan retained an atmosphere that has one and a half times the surface pressure of Earth's atmosphere but is held by much less gravity. They calculated that to retain such an atmosphere, Titan must replenish the atmospheric gases as fast as it loses them into space. The loss to space is caused by its weak gravitational field, which is one-seventh that of the Earth. The only source for these replenishment gases had to be the moon's supposedly frozen interior.

One gas of particular interest in Titan's atmosphere was methane, because it contains the hydrocarbons that are the basic chemical elements required for living cells. The methane gas in Titan's atmosphere must come from either a subsurface reservoir or there are biological processes taking place on or near the moon's surface that form this gas. Data from the landing module has shown that there are no biological processes taking place. This is what would be expected at the frigid average temperature of -179°C on the moon's surface.

The present scientific explanation for the replenishment of the methane is based on a layer of clathrate hydrate under the surface acting as the source of methane. This layer would have formed somewhere beneath the surface when the moon originally cooled from a liquid mixture of its chemical compounds. This theory based on evolutionary time scales required that sufficient subsurface heat is still generated to release enough methane to maintain its presence in the atmosphere after the billions of years since the moon was supposedly formed.[10] The CM-model requires only that enough heat is generated to release the gas after a period of less than ten thousand years.

Comparison with Earth's Atmosphere

Large deposits of clathrate hydrate have been found on Earth beneath the oceans and even certain landmasses.[11] Beside these deposits, hydrocarbon gases have been found in large reservoirs within the crust. The question these discoveries brought up is why Earth's atmosphere does not contain a large quantity of hydrocarbon gases similar to Titan. That question is answered by the amount of free oxygen present on Earth that Titan does not have. On Titan, oxygen was not detected directly and could exist only in frozen water or carbon dioxide below the surface.

We speculated that the original atmosphere of Earth could have contained a large quantity of hydrocarbon gases. This would have provided some of the fuel for fires in the atmosphere on the third day. The fires would have converted the hydrocarbons into other gases and solid byproducts. As stated earlier in this chapter, most of the products of hydrocarbon gases burning in the presence of oxygen and hydrogen are visually transparent gases found in the Earth's atmosphere. The solid products would have served as fertilizer in the topsoil for plants.

The First Four Days

SUMMARY

During the night of the third day, seas first covered the whole surface of the Earth after God commanded the seawater to gather in one place. At the same time this original ocean was forming, the original atmosphere also formed from gases being released out of the same or other chambers in Earth's hardening crust. Next, God continued this surface-forming miracle by commanding at least one landmass to rise out of the crust and appear above sea level. As a result of that command, the seawater retreated to its newly formed basin whose boundaries were the shores of the dry land.

The granite foundations of at least one continent were established on top of the original crust, which still retained underground seawater reservoirs. According to the CM-model, the foundations of the continent were formed by a large pluton of molten rock pushing up through the crust and spreading out on its surface, displacing the seawater. The granite contained both mantle rock compounds and sedimentary rock compounds in proportions related to the depth where the samples were taken in the formation. This indicates the granite formed at one time. The process of crystallization of zircons that are found in most granite rocks indicates that they formed rapidly. Also, the recently measured amount of helium in zircons found in granite rocks limits the age of the granite to thousands of years.

As the hot seawater ran off the raised land, it picked up a large amount of broken-up and eroded rock and deposited it along its route and into the ocean basin as sediment. From the top layer of sediment, soil was formed most likely with the addition of fertilizer chemicals deposited by the burning of the atmosphere. God or the angels he commanded had to have prepared the soil, since mankind were not yet available for this task. At the upper ends of the valleys, springs of fresh water formed and provided the water for rivers and lakes that watered the newly formed soil.

It was apparent from the CMA that the atmosphere did not remain the thick dark cloud described in Job 38:9. It had to be transformed on the third day into its final habitable mixture from its original composition, which consisted of gases and dust that would not support life. We speculated that this transformation was accomplished by burning of the original chemical elements and compounds in the air. This burning may have provided the light for the daylight period on the third day.

Another possible source for the visible light on the third day we proposed in the CM-model was a cosmic source. On the third day, the second white hole at the center of the galaxy could have pointed in a direction so that light and cosmic rays arrived on the Earth for half a day, possibly causing an aurora surrounding the Earth. The white hole would have rotated around while forming the second major arm of the spiral Milky Way galaxy. Both sources of light we proposed for the third day were one-time events that would have required God's control of the physical processes and their rates in the universe.

Conclusion of Habitat Preparation on the Earth

The CM-model has now been developed to explain a fully prepared surface of the Earth for establishing a habitat for plants, animals, and mankind. The soil was prepared for growing plants, and the watering system was installed. The atmosphere was transformed into the air that supports both plant and animal life. God had completed the surface preparations of air, sea, and land with rapid maturing of all functions to support a paradise for mankind on the planet called Earth.

CHAPTER 6

Divine Action 5: Making Plants Sprout and Grow

DAY 3B: ADDING PLANT LIFE TO THE EARTH'S SURFACE HABITAT

THE PREVIOUS CHAPTER described God's actions on the third day that began the preparation of the Earth's surface for a habitat in which his creatures would live. Once the seas, dry land, and atmosphere were established, God began the basic ecosystem for that habitat. Still required for a perfect habitat were the production of food for the future living creatures and a source of energy to sustain it. He established the food production originally in the afternoon of the third day with divine action 5. It took another of God's miracles on the fourth day to make the sun into the provider of heat and light energy that his creation still required (the topic of the next chapter).

For the CM-model, we speculated in the previous chapter that God prepared the soil by fertilizing and tilling it. In miracle 5, God commanded the newly prepared soil to sprout every kind of grass and fruit tree. This vegetation grew rapidly from the soil and covered the land surface. Its coverage most likely extended a short distance into the rivers and lakes as it does now. We infer from the CMA (v. 30) that God also provided plant-like food for creatures that would live in the oceans, rivers, and lakes where plants don't sprout from the soil.

All the plants and plant-like organisms were originally designed so that they rapidly matured and continued to reproduce their kind. This miracle took place on the afternoon of the third day. These plants and plant-like organisms matured and produced leaves, seeds, and fruit in less than a day. They were fully mature by the end of the day with seeds and fruit already ripened. God's main purpose for this vegetation was for it to provide a continual food source for all the living creatures—including mankind—as God stated in the CMA (vv. 29–30). This miracle was also alluded to in Psalm 104:27–28. (See also the special section on Closely Related Bible Verses below for more details on plants as food.)

CLOSELY RELATED BIBLE VERSES TO MIRACLE 5

Genesis 1:29–30

Then God said, "Behold, I have given you every plant yielding seed that is on the surface of all the earth, and every tree which has fruit yielding seed; it shall be food for you; and to every beast of the earth and to every bird of the sky and to every thing that moves on the earth which has life, I have given every green plant for food': and it was so."

—Gen. 1:29–30

These verses are included in the CMA but do not report a miracle of creating or making. Instead, the author reported God's directive to mankind that he had provided all the plants as a food source for his living creatures. God's purpose for making the plants and plant-like organisms was for them to be food producers. The establishment of the plant-growth process started an ecosystem that two days later would include all living organisms on Earth. Plants and all their associated organisms that began to grow on the third day were miraculous gifts from God. They have continued as a major source of food for animals and mankind ever since the third day.

Psalm 104:27–28

They all [living creatures] wait for You [LORD] to give them their food in due season. You give to them, they gather it up; You open Your hand, they are satisfied with good.

—Ps. 104:27–28

Like the references in previous chapters from Psalm 104, these verses alluded to an event that occurred during the week of creating and making. Specifically, these verses allude to God's directive to mankind on the sixth day as reported in the CMA (vv. 29–30). He is the one who provided the plants as food producers for mankind and all living creatures.

Numbers 17:7–9

So Moses deposited the rods before the LORD in the tent of the testimony. Now on the next day Moses went into the tent of the testimony; and behold, the rod of Aaron for the house of Levi had sprouted and put forth buds and produced blossoms, and it bore ripe almonds. Moses then brought out all the rods from the presence of the LORD to all the sons of Israel; and they looked, and each man took his rod.

—Num. 17:7–9

We should not be surprised that God could make plants sprout and come to maturity in less than a day as reported in the CMA. He did so again in Moses' time when he caused a dead wooden walking stick to sprout, produce buds and blossoms, and finally bear ripe almonds, all in one night. We speculate that there must have been petals on the floor of the tent that housed the Ark of the Covenant that next morning. God did this miracle without the rod being planted into the ground for its roots to grow.

OTHER BIBLICAL REFERENCES TO MIRACLE 5

Genesis 2:8–9

The LORD God planted a garden toward the east, in Eden; and there He placed the man whom He had formed. Out of the ground the LORD God caused to grow every tree that is pleasing to the sight and good for food; the tree of life also in the midst of the garden, and the tree of the knowledge of good and evil.

—Gen. 2:8–9

These verses confirmed that the main purpose for trees was to provide food. But trees also had the purpose to provide landscaping that was pleasing to the eye. God planted two special trees in the Garden of Eden and caused them to grow. One provided a source of perpetual life for mankind if they ate the fruit. The other provided a test of mankind's obedience to God's authority. God likely removed or buried these two special trees during the Genesis Flood.

Psalm 104:14–17

He causes the grass to grow for the cattle, and vegetation for the labor of man, so that he may bring forth food from the earth, and wine which makes man's heart glad, so that he may make his face glisten with oil, and food which sustains man's heart. The trees of the LORD drink their fill, the cedars of Lebanon which He planted, where the birds build their nests, and the stork, whose home is the fir trees.

—Ps. 104:14–17

We referenced the initial verses of Psalm 104 in previous chapters as a hymn of praise to the Creator for his creation and all its benefits. In these verses, the author provided snapshots that allude to the purpose of the plants that God caused to sprout and grow on the third day. Two plant types—grasses and trees—are pictured in their role of food providers that complement the CMA report. In verse 14, the snapshots confirmed the purpose of the grasses. They were food for the grazing animals and provided grains and vegetables that mankind could plant and cultivate for their use. In verse 15, products from tree kinds are pictured, such as wine made from fruit of vines and olive oil made from fruit trees. Mankind used these products daily in addition to eating the fruit. The next two verses (vv. 16–17) pictured trees prospering and providing habitat for the birds.

More General References

There were few references to plant life in the Bible, mainly because plants were a physical product of the land, and their main purpose was food production. This was firmly established from the beginning (Gen. 1:29–30). However, God designed the seed of plants and its reproductive capability as a model for the way animals and mankind also reproduce. This reproductive process was also spoken of in 1 Corinthians 15:35–38 as an analogy to the hope of eternal life for mankind. This analogy pointed out that a seed needs to first die (all its internal chemical activity stopped). But after the seed is buried in the ground, the chemical activity restarts, and the plant sprouts to live again with a new God-given body.

Another reference to plants is in Genesis 3:17–18. Either some new plants sprouted and grew or some original kinds were modified and became thorns and thistles. God did this as part of the curse on the ground to punish Adam for his sin. This emphasized the close relationship and dependence of plants on the land to which they are attached.

In the religious life of the Israelites, plant products were offered to God for memorial offerings (Leviticus 2:2) and thank offerings (7:12). God required these offerings to remind his people that he provided the bountiful harvests that fed them and all the animals.

SCIENTIFIC TERMINOLOGY

Cell-Based Life

The basic building block God used to make a living organism like a plant or animal was a cell. The simplest single-celled organisms are called bacteria. They have been found everywhere on Earth, including in the oceans, in the soil, and even within plants and animals. A cell wall encloses all the molecular components and chemical processes that cause bacteria cells to live, as shown in Illustration 6.1. These simplest organisms are complex when compared to lifeless objects. They contain many naturally occurring atomic elements and involve many chemical processes. They were designed to vary greatly in their form and function. Over 4,800 different types of bacteria have been identified.

A cell that is subdivided into compartments forms more complex single-celled organisms called protists. Each compartment serves a unique function within these cells. The coordination required between compartments adds complexity to their cell design when compared to a bacteria cell. Amoeba, diatoms, and some algae are considered single-celled protists. Protist cells have been found that contain some, but not necessarily all, of the compartments that are found in the complex cells of multi-celled plants or animals.

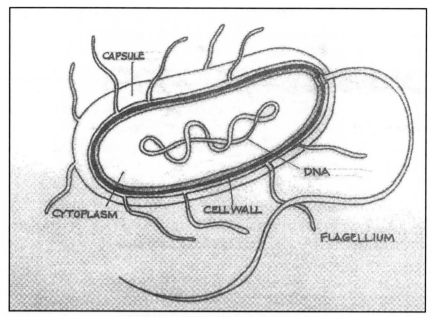

ILLUSTRATION 6.1: Single-celled bacteria.

The protists are followed in the hierarchy of complexity by the simplest multi-cellular organisms. Both certain types of algae and most types of an organism called fungi are multi-celled but are not considered fully plants. They lack one or more of the compartments found in a typical plant cell. Scientists who support evolution have attempted to establish an evolutionary link between the single-celled and these sub-plant multi-celled organisms based on complexity of their cells. Such attempts have been unsuccessful because each of these organisms has been shown to be of a unique design and reproduce only their own kind.

All multi-celled organisms such as fungi, plants, and animals have cells that are compartmented. Besides controlling their own internal processes, it was necessary for cells to communicate with other cells to control the growth and reproduction of the whole organism. The compartments within a plant cell are like rooms in a house. Each compartment is separated by a membrane that controls what chemical molecules go into and out of it. There are four main types of compartments that are identified by their contents and function. The remainder of the cell is filled with a liquid called cytoplasm.

Plant Cell Compartments

The internal structure of a typical plant cell is shown in Illustration 6.2. The nucleus is the control center of the cell and includes its memory components. It can be modeled as the computer that controls an automated production facility. The memory components—genes and chromosomes—are confined to the nucleus, and they retain the blueprint of the plant cell for production of new cells and also the reproduction of the entire plant. The memory components are made from ribonucleic acid (RNA) and deoxyribonucleic acid (DNA).

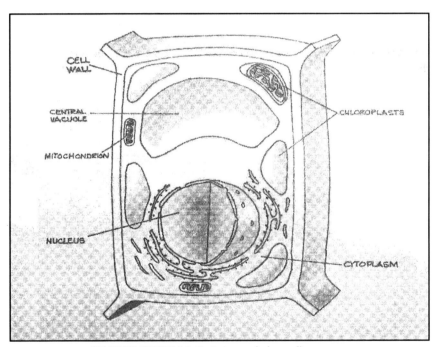

ILLUSTRATION 6.2: Basic internal plant cell structure.

The largest compartment, the central vacuole, can be modeled as a warehouse. The cell vacuole is used to store the raw materials such as water molecules and chemical ions for its production lines. It is also used to store products that the cell manufactures such as sugars and starches. The use of the chemical compounds and ions stored in the vacuole is coordinated by the control center in the nucleus with all the production sites in the cell.

Many smaller compartments called chloroplasts and mitochondria are strategically placed around the nucleus and vacuole. The chloroplasts can be modeled as manufacturing facilities for carbohydrates in the plant cell. In these facilities, energy from sunlight is captured and converted to electro-chemical bonds of complex carbohydrates such as sugars, starches, and cellulose. Mitochondria are designed to provide the electrical power that drives all the processes within the cell. They can be modeled as batteries where energy that was stored in chemical bonds is converted back into electricity when added power is required by the manufacturing processes of the cell.

Plant Life

Plants were the first product God made during creation week with the capability of changing their size and controlling the multiple chemical processes that occur within them. Plants were designed to grow in size by constructing new cells and adding them to their structure. The processes involved follow a design or blueprint, a copy of which is stored in the nucleus of every cell in the plant. The overall design of most plants included: a) the conversion of light and carbon dioxide from the atmosphere into stored chemical energy in carbohydrates; b) conversion of chemical energy into electrical energy and limited mechanical motion; c) production of new cells, for growth and replacement, and also the special reproduction cells found in seeds; and d) the release of the byproduct oxygen into the atmosphere. The design of each plant was perfect for it to fulfill its main purpose of changing air, soil, and water into food that animals and humans can digest.

Plant life was made different from animal life in that plants were made entirely of the chemical elements found in the air, ground, or water. When God commanded the plants to sprout and grow, he did not create something in them from nothing. In animals, God created a consciousness that allowed them to be mobile and change their location and environment. Plants are designed to be dependent on the environment at their location. The vast majority of plant varieties are permanently attached to the ground during their whole life cycle except when they are dormant in the form of seeds. But even seeds were not designed to make changes in their environment as animals can. When plant seeds or spores do move, it is due to a host, such as the wind, animals, or insects.

Plant Nutrients and Products

All the nutrients for plants are extracted from their environment and consist of molecules of gaseous elements or solid and liquid chemical compounds. These nutrients are used to construct more complex molecules called carbohydrates and proteins. The main chemicals used by plants in their production processes include water, carbon dioxide, and nitrogen molecules from the air, and chemical compounds made from elements such as sulfur, iron, iodine, and phosphorus from the soil.

God designed all green-leafed plants to have an internal process called photosynthesis that helps produce complex carbohydrates such as sugar, starch, and cellulose. Sugars and starches store electrical energy in their chemical bonds so that it can be used by the cell or stored for animals to eat. Cells use cellulose as the building material from which to form cell walls. The genetic code to manufacture the chlorophyll that the plant uses in the photosynthesis process had to be provided at the beginning of this plant life.

All internal cell processes are controlled by another cell product called an enzyme that is made from proteins. Proteins are made of large chains of amino acids linked in a very specific sequence. There are twenty known amino acids, but their use in thousands of different sequences in proteins (like letters forming words and words forming sentences) form the basis for the large variety of living organisms.

The complex processes that first produce the proteins and then combine them into unique sequences to make the enzymes within a cell cannot be described in a simple manner. These processes have been found to be so complex that scientists still do not understand them. Such a complex system of chemical reactions is required for the production of enzymes within a cell that they could not have evolved on their own. It would have been similar to a computer first building its components and then programming itself. The process could only have been designed and built by a very intelligent designer-maker at the beginning of all plant life. We refer the reader to any college-level biology textbook, such as *The Living World*, for further information on how proteins and enzymes are made by cells in plants and animals.[1]

An Ecosystem

Ecology is defined as the study of the interactions of living organisms with one another and with their physical environment. An ecosystem can be defined as a community of living organisms that interact within the environment they inhabit. We speculate that the ecosystem that existed at the end of the third day included a community of plants, fungi, bacteria, and protists within the habitat of land and sea on the surface of the planet Earth. The author of the CMA did not directly mention fungi, bacteria, and protists. But it can be inferred from their interaction with plants and animals (both on land and in the seas) that they were necessary from the beginning for the ecosystem to be complete and self-sustaining.

THE CM-MODEL

The CM-model so far has the soil prepared, a watering system installed, and the optimum mixture of gases established in the atmosphere. The soil preparation included the speculated fertilization byproducts of the burning atmosphere being mixed into the top soil with tilling by supernatural means. Springs from under the ground that formed lakes, small streams, and larger rivers supplied water to the soil. Water vapor in the form of a mist that rose into the air also contributed to the water supply (Gen. 2:6), especially higher on the mountainsides. God's next divine action most likely took place on the afternoon of the third day. This divine action started an ecosystem in the surface habitat being prepared for animals and mankind.

Divine Act 5

Let the dry land sprout vegetation, both grassy plants yielding seeds of their kind and trees bearing fruit that contains seeds of their kind.
—Gen. 1:11, paraphrased

In this act, God commanded the ground to sprout vegetation that grew to cover the newly prepared surface of the dry land. Significantly, God did not create plants fully grown but only commanded that the soil sprout them. For the CM-model, we speculate that the response to the command took place in a two-stage process.

In the first stage, God formed plant seeds from the chemical molecules found in the soil. Then this was followed immediately by God causing the seeds to rapidly sprout and plants to grow to maturity as they continue to do in nature today. The growth had to take place at an accelerated rate to meet God's timeline. According to the timeline reported in the CMA, the vegetation sprouted and grew to maturity in the remainder of that same day. Only God can perform this type of miracle as he demonstrated again for the Israelites in the wilderness (Num. 17:8) when the tree branch (walking stick) sprouted leaves, buds, and fruit overnight, and it was not even attached to the ground by roots.

Plant Construction

Most plants are constructed out of millions of microscopic living cells. These cells can be described as living in the sense that they contain ongoing chemical processes that were designed to allow the plant to grow and reproduce. They are not living in the same sense that animals and man were created to live with the breath of life in them. The chemical processes in plant cells did not evolve in a natural environment as supporters of evolution would have everyone believe. The structure of a plant cell and the chemical processes taking place in them are far too complex to develop on their own. God designed and built plant cells for the specific purpose of allowing the plants to grow and reproduce their own kind as food for animals and mankind.

Another indication of intelligent design, internal processes of plants run in cycles that are directly linked to the environment surrounding the plant. Plants accomplish this adaptation without a central nervous system. For example, the sugar and starch production in a green-leafed plant is linked to the cycle of day and night. Another example, the overall life cycle of many plants is linked to the seasons of the year. The cycle starts as the plant sprouts from a seed in spring, then it grows to maturity during the summer, and finally produces many more seeds in the fall. This type of plant usually dies and the seeds are dormant during the winter months. But each new seed it produces repeats such a cycle annually.

Construction of the Ecosystem

The CMA mentions only two major kinds of vegetation that sprouted and grew after God's command. These kinds consisted of seed-bearing grasses and fruit-bearing trees. For a self-sustaining ecosystem, we speculated above that other plant-like organisms were also necessary. God designed and constructed these unmentioned plant-like organisms of the ecosystem to operate in perfect harmony with plants.

Plant-like organisms in the ecosystem are required by some of the plant varieties that are mentioned in the CMA. For an example, plants called legumes, a grassy kind, have bacteria in nodules on their roots. The bacteria are required to break down the molecular bonds of nitrogen gas found in the soil. The resulting nitrogen ions are then passed from the bacteria to the plant root. The legume plant uses the nitrogen ions to construct proteins. An example of a plant-like organism that many trees require is the growth of fungi on or near their roots. Over 80 percent of tree species depend on a fungus to supply their roots with sufficient quantities of minerals, such as phosphorus, from the soil. Without the fungi, the trees would not be able to obtain enough nutrients to sustain their normal growth rate, much less mature in less than twelve hours on the third day.

Another example for plant-like organisms that are required in the ecosystem is food production for marine animals. Marine animals, such as whales and many fish, feed on several varieties of protists. These animals cannot reach plants that grow from the ground so that they can feed on them. God prepared the underwater ecosystem with their food consisting of algae, diatoms, and plankton (a combination of protists and bacteria). Many of these plant-like organisms grow in both sea and fresh water.

The bacteria, fungi, and protists were plant-like organisms designed to grow and reproduce themselves independent of the other plants and animals. But they have symbiotic relationships with plants and animals where each provides a service directly to the other. All the living organisms in a local environment play an essential role in plant and animal survival for the perfect ecosystem on the surface of Earth. What God did to make it imperfect after mankind sinned (Gen. 3:18) is not specifically reported in the Bible. But scientific research has shown that the plant and plant-like organism portion of the ecosystem has deteriorated and continues to do so.

As with the other miracles during creation week, the CMA provides little detail on how the planting and growing of plants took place. From scientific research on plant biology and how they grow, interact, and reproduce today, we can infer that the entire ecosystem on which plant life depended was made all at once. The different interacting and symbiotic parts could not have functioned properly alone for very long or at an accelerated rate. Every niche of the ecosystem on the surface of Earth was filled rapidly with plants and plant-like organisms so that nothing was missing in a perfect and complete habitat (Gen. 1:12).

Cell Reproduction for Growth and Replacement

The information required for the production of all the different cells in a plant from an embryo cell is coded in the cell's genes. Both the growth and repair information required by the plant had to be programmed with their DNA into the first cell of each type of plant. Seeds do not gain information on their own while they are dormant or when they become alive.

The DNA and RNA are both located in the nucleus of the plant cells. RNA molecules decode the information stored in the genes and chromosomes in order to make enzymes. The enzymes in turn are moved to their appointed compartment in the cell. From there they control cell development, the manufacturing processes in a cell, and cell reproduction. The nucleus of most plant cells is less than five micrometers in diameter (100 times smaller than the period at the end of this sentence). The information stored in this small amount of genetic material is so complex that it could not have evolved on its own. Even the simplest single-celled organism has four nucleic acid molecules arranged in thousands of sequences in perfect order within its DNA and RNA for the organism to live and duplicate the information for new organisms of their kind.

The DNA molecule is in the shape of a double helix having two connected strings of genes in identical order. A single string of genes is called a chromosome. Non-reproductive plant cells are designed with RNA that is capable of decoding only the portion of the chromosomes that is required to control their own duplication. This process can be modeled as their having a software program that reads only the part of memory that is required to carry out this limited internal function.

In cell production, RNA molecules are designed to take the information from a portion of the DNA molecule and use it to direct the construction of a duplicate cell. This process is accomplished by cell division where everything in the parent cell is first duplicated and then the cell is divided into two cells. How the cell first sensed the need to duplicate itself remains a mystery and one reason why mankind have not copied the reproduction system of plants for use in machines. It can be described as an inherent process designed into the plant cell so that new cells replace worn out cells or are added for overall plant growth. Another mystery that has not been solved is how the RNA molecule acts on only the portion of the DNA molecule it was designed to decode.

The accelerated growth rate of the plants on the third day must be considered a miracle where even processes within living cells were accelerated to meet God's purpose for the plants. The plants were destined to produce food for animals by the fifth and sixth day. For example, a red oak tree that normally takes twenty years or more to mature and produce acorns for squirrels and other wildlife produced them in less than a day. The carbohydrate production and cell division processes in the tree cells must have operated perfectly to achieve the growth rate that took place. For a tree like the red oak, this growth rate must have been greater than 1,000 times the present rate. They normally grow two feet per year and reach heights greater than 100 feet. But their growth rate is dependent on their environment, and that was changed when the land was cursed after mankind sinned.

We would infer from the CMA that Adam would have seen blossom petals on the ground under fruit and nut trees on the sixth day. But we speculate that God may have already slowed their growth rate with all the other natural processes at the end of the fourth day. Only the almighty Creator could have achieved this miracle of accelerated growth and rapid maturing.

Forming Seeds for Reproduction

Most multi-celled organisms like plants were designed to reproduce by forming seeds. This can be considered a form of sexual reproduction, and the majority of both plants and animals share this process. In plant seeds, a dormant embryo cell is placed within a hardened shell when the seed is formed. This embryo cell, microscopic in size, contained all the genetic information for the grasses or trees to grow and ultimately reproduce their kind. The information passed along includes both the design for the plant's external structure and all the internal chemical processes within its cells.

Special cells within a plant produce the pollen and eggs that produce a new plant from an embryo cell. These cells are designed to have the RNA to decode the entire DNA information required to make copies of every type of cell in the plant. When the pollen and eggs are later combined, the resulting embryo cell containing this information is placed in a seed. The process of duplication followed by these special cells is much more complex than simple cell division. It will be described in more detail below as scientific evidence that supports the CM-model and intelligent design of plants.

Plant Kinds

The author of the CMA reported that God caused two categories of plants to sprout from the ground on the third day—the grass kinds and the tree kinds. Grass kinds yielding seeds most likely included the typical grasses that provide ground cover, the cereal grain plants such as wheat and oats, and all the garden vegetables. We speculate that some of these plants were capable of reproducing themselves through their roots, in addition to their seeds. This was a form of asexual reproduction that greatly increased their reproduction capability.

We infer from the CMA and Genesis 2:9 that the fruit-tree category included all trees, including those trees and bushes that are currently used only for landscaping. Besides the common fruit and nut trees, this category would have also included the conifer trees like pine, spruce, or cedar that produce seeds in cones rather than fruit. Even vines like grapes, berries, tomatoes, and melons would be considered tree kinds, because they bear fruit with seeds in it.

Evolution Fails to Explain Plant Life

Scientists who support evolution have promoted a theory that the development of the complex chemical reactions for each of the processes involved in plant life developed in many small steps. They claim the symbiotic relationships between different organisms developed in a similar manner. The main problem with that theory is the lack of an explanation for the survival of an organism without all its internal processes operating at the same time and without its symbiotic relationships already established. Scientific research into these processes and relationships has shown that if any are missing or even malfunctioning, the plant dies or cannot reproduce.

Also, these scientists have been unable to find any evidence that small increases of complexity actually took place. In general, the evidence found in nature contradicts the hypothesis of the evolutionary development of a plant. For example, fossils all show remains of fully developed plants that have died. Degrading (stopping the plants' internal processes) caused death. No fossil has been found that exhibited a transitional development of a new process in a living organism.[2] However, all symbiotic relationships between two different living organisms are required by both to survive.

Researchers also have found that the sexual reproduction process used by plants is similar to that used by animals. Scientists who support evolution have found it difficult to explain how the same process could have evolved in both plants and animals. Their options are limited to showing that two independent evolutions of the same process took place or that a transfer of the process occurred between animals and plants. No scientific evidence has been found to support either option. The DNA in the genes of plants is not found in animals. Evidence has not been found that plants and animals ever contained the same genes to control their reproduction. An Intelligent Designer and Creator who used a similar design for programming the sexual reproduction capability into both plant and animal DNA must be considered as the most realistic explanation.

SCIENTIFIC EVIDENCE THAT SUPPORTS THE CM-MODEL

We chose three areas of plant biology research to show evidence that supports the CM-model and intelligent design of vegetation and the other living organisms made on the third day. These three examples from the complex ecosystem on Earth illustrate that: a) only a perfectly designed chemical process called photosynthesis would allow green-leafed plants to grow and mature rapidly, b) only a perfectly designed and complex reproductive process would allow plants to rapidly propagate their kind to feed all the living creatures, and c) only by symbiotic relationships between plants and other living organisms could they sustain their growth, food production, and reproduction rates.

Photosynthesis II

Researchers have found that photosynthesis is one of the most important of the internal processes in green-leafed plants. The chloroplasts in cells of these plants are chemical factories that produce carbohydrates such as cellulose, sugars, and starches. The production lines for these products first use the photosynthesis process to break down water into hydrogen and oxygen ions using energy from sunlight. The hydrogen ions are then combined with carbon and oxygen extracted from carbon dioxide to form the final products. During the process, extra oxygen molecules are formed and released to the atmosphere as a byproduct.

The photosynthesis II process is confined to the chloroplasts within the plant cells. A unique green chemical compound called chlorophyll is produced in the chloroplasts by special enzymes as the cell develops. Chlorophyll is optimally designed to act as the catalyst for the photochemical reaction in photosynthesis as shown in Illustration 6.3. It also provides plant leaves with their green color by reflecting green light while absorbing other visible wavelengths.

Scientists in the laboratory have not duplicated the chemical process of photosynthesis II because it is very complex and operates at the atomic level. For example, a water molecule is broken down in several stages by the chlorophyll. These stages are required because a single photon with enough energy to do the job in one step also has enough energy to destroy the plant cell. Four photons of visible sunlight are required to convert two molecules of water into their constituents of four hydrogen atoms and two oxygen atoms.

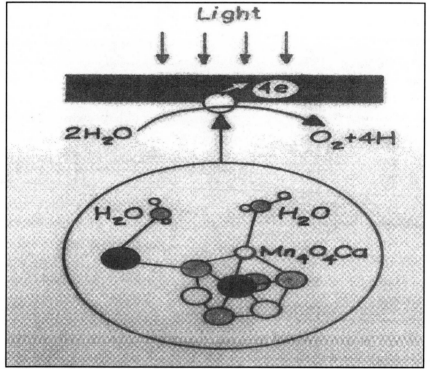

ILLUSTRATION 6.3: The photosynthesis II process and the chlorophyll molecule.

The storage of intermediate-level energies from the first three photons is done in a central core arrangement of the chlorophyll molecule. This core is made of three manganese atoms, four oxygen atoms, and a calcium atom in a cubic structure that is attached to another manganese atom. This cubic structure captures the energy of a photon in the first three stages of the process and passes it to the lone manganese atom so that it gives up one of its electrons. It took the energy from the three visible photons to remove this electron. That same electron energy is required to separate the first hydrogen atom out of a water molecule.

The core requires energy from the fourth photon to split up the remaining OH radical into a hydrogen ion and an oxygen ion. At the moment the OH radical is split, a second water molecule is held in the exact location where the newly freed oxygen ion can attach itself to the oxygen atom of this water molecule. When these oxygen ions are attached to each other, the two hydrogen atoms of the second water molecule are set free. The margin for error in the whole photosynthesis II process must be much less than the size of the atoms involved. The chlorophyll molecule must be perfectly designed for this process. No other molecule known to man would work in this process.

The four hydrogen ions are freed by photosynthesis II for the next stage of carbohydrate manufacturing. The hydrogen ions are transported to another part of the cell where they are stored until nighttime. At night, the leaves of the plant absorb carbon dioxide from the air. In the plant cell, the hydrogen ions are brought into contact with the carbon dioxide molecules, causing them to form a bond with the carbon and oxygen atoms in a process called carbon fixation. Carbohydrates such as sugars are long strings of bonded carbon, hydrogen, and oxygen produced by this process.

Besides the complexity of the photosynthesis process itself, the continuous repair capability of the plant cells has to be taken into account. Any damaged part, such as a broken chlorophyll molecule, is replaced with a new one when required. Mankind have not designed a robotic system with such a self-repair capability. The Intelligent Designer designed and built a robust repair system into plants that will continue to help plants provide food for all his creatures until the end of time.

The complex nature of the carbohydrate manufacturing processes must be considered strong evidence that they were designed by the most Intelligent Designer that exists. This tiny photochemical factory was designed to operate perfectly from the beginning. On the first day of existence, we speculate that it operated at many times the present production rates. The high production rates were necessary to supply the energy and material for plants to grow and mature in less than a day. For tall trees to grow to their full size in such a short time would require more than 1,000 times the present rate. No one has determined what the food production limit of the plants would have been under the optimum conditions that existed on their first day.

In the CM-model, we speculated that God made other plant-like organisms on the same day as plants. This speculation is supported by the fact that some of these organisms (algae such as seaweed and pond scum) also make their own carbohydrates by a photosynthesis process. They are the food for many marine animals. Even the most brilliant scientists have not duplicated the whole process in a laboratory, because it takes place at atomic and molecular distances. Without a perfect and complete design, the process would not work. For more detailed information on the photosynthesis process, see the article by Jonathan Sarfati.[3]

Plant Reproduction

Most plant kinds (90 percent) use seeds to reproduce. Special cells found in the flowers of the plants produce these seeds. Both male and female reproduction organs are normally located in the flower. The male organs are called stamen, and they produce pollen. The female organ is called the carpel and includes the ovary where the egg cells are formed and fertilized to produce the embryo cell that is placed in the seed. The carpel also forms the fruit that contains the seeds of fruit-bearing trees. Evidence for an elegant design is found in the complex nature of this reproduction process to provide a perfect new plant of the same kind that produced the seed.

Both the cells that produce the pollen and the eggs are programmed differently than the other cells in the plant that duplicate themselves by cell division. These germ cells, called gametes, must first duplicate the two chromosomes of their DNA like all the other cells. But instead of dividing the nucleus and cell after this initial duplication, two new steps are added into the reproduction process. First, the four chromosomes that resulted are brought together physically so that they can exchange genes. Then after that process is completed, the nucleus and cell are divided for the first time.

Two chromosomes are still contained in the DNA molecule of each resulting cell after this first cell division. The second added step, called reduction, prepares the cells for sexual reproduction. The nucleus of both these intermediate cells is divided a second time without first duplicating their chromosomes. This division forms four cells, each with a single chromosome in its DNA molecule, and they are either pollen or egg cells. Later, at the time of fertilization, the single chromosome in the pollen and an egg are brought together so that they form a complete molecule of DNA that has two chromosomes. The completed DNA is formed in the nucleus of an embryo cell that is placed into a seed.

This process has been continuous for thousands of years, and billions of plants have been produced. Only a perfect design could maintain such a production line for that length of time. Most college-level biology textbooks like *The Living World* by George Johnson can be used as references for a more detailed description of the complex reproduction process and its perfect results.[4]

Symbiosis of Plants with Other Living Organisms

There are many examples of plants having a symbiotic relationship with the other living organisms found in Earth's ecosystem. We chose three examples as scientific evidence that symbiotic relationships did not evolve but must have been designed and built into the plant DNA for it to live and reproduce. The three examples described below are the symbiotic relationships between: a) legume plants and the bacteria within their roots, b) most trees and fungi that attach to their roots (called mycorrhizae association), and c) yucca plants that can reproduce only with the help of the yucca moth.

Legume Plants and Bacteria

The occurrence of single-celled bacteria in the roots of legume plants is well documented.[5] The rhizobium bacteria are always found in nodules that grow on the roots of this plant type. The plant root is designed to supply the source of food in the form of carbohydrates for the bacteria to live and grow in these nodules. The bacteria in the nodules have been shown to take nitrogen and hydrogen from the air in the soil around the root nodule and construct ammonia molecules in a process called nitrogen fixing. Nitrogen fixing is considered a difficult process because the two nitrogen atoms in a molecule of air are triple-bonded to each other (share three electrons). Plants on their own are designed to absorb easier-to-use nitrogen compounds from the soil that are in contact with their roots. But nitrogen fixing by bacteria is required by the plant when the soil next to its root becomes depleted of these nitrogen compounds. This depletion has occurred in certain soils in as short a time as one growing season.

The rhizobium is designed specifically to manufacture a unique enzyme that has the capability to break the tough nitrogen bonds. The enzyme splits the nitrogen molecule into two nitrogen ions and then makes them into ammonia molecules by attaching four hydrogen atoms (from two molecules of hydrogen) to each ion. The ammonia is a compound that the plant root can absorb and the plant cells can use to manufacture proteins. Excess ammonia is returned to the soil for other nearby plants to use. This enzyme is made of large proteins and provides an efficient natural method for breaking the molecular nitrogen bond. Manmade methods for making ammonia out of the air have always required high temperature (540°C) and pressure (300 atmospheres).

Each legume plant is designed to allow a specific type of bacteria into its root as it grows. The plants had to be designed and programmed with genes to set up their relationship with this specific type of bacteria. Without the bacteria, these plants would soon die off from lack of nitrogen in a form they can use. Because these plants were designed as a major food source for animals and mankind, Earth's whole ecosystem is greatly dependent on the tiny single-celled organisms called rhyzobium to help provide a continual food supply.

As support of the CM-model, legume plants could only have grown from a seed to full maturity in less than a day if they had the bacteria in their roots. The level of nitrogen-rich compounds in the soil near enough to the plant roots would have been depleted rapidly. At normal growth rates, the nitrogen can be depleted in a single growing season, even when rain replenishes the supply. Without the bacteria in their roots, the legume plants would have died by nitrogen starvation before they could have produced their seeds at the accelerated rate required.

Tree Roots and Fungi

Symbiotic relationships between tree roots and fungi are called mycorrhizae associations. They are another example of a design that was imposed on living organisms in the ecosystem so that the whole system continues to function. These fungi act as extensions of a tree-root system. The fungi are fast-growing and can penetrate the soil much more easily than the tree roots themselves. Some fungi are designed also to penetrate the tree root to deliver minerals like phosphorus directly into the root. Others are designed to transport certain minerals close enough to a root so it can absorb them. In return, the fungi use the organic carbohydrate products given off by the tree root as nutrients to live and grow.

Without the rapid access to the minerals that the fungi provide, the growth rate of the trees would be reduced significantly. The trees also would have remained smaller in size and produced less fruit. The whole ecosystem that depends on the trees to provide food for animals and mankind is aided by the acceleration of tree development due to the fungi. The original design for both the tree and the fungi provided for a mutually beneficial association that could not have evolved slowly over time. Only the Intelligent Designer and Creator could have taken into account all the factors required for this association of unlike organisms to function. Scientists have just recently begun to unravel the mysteries of how this complex system functions.[6] Again for the CM-model, this association would have been necessary to support the accelerated growth of trees on the third day.

Yucca Plants and the Yucca Moth

There are 40–50 species of yucca plants that make up the agavaceae family. The family includes different types of plants such as perennials, shrubs, and trees. All of the members of the family are known for their rosettes of evergreen, tough, sword-shaped leaves. They are native to most of the western regions of North America and the Southeastern United States.

All the species of yucca are designed to depend on a unique method for their pollination. A specific moth, called a yucca moth, is genetically programmed so that it stuffs a little ball of pollen into the cup-shaped opening (stigma) in the carpel of each flower on a yucca plant. At the same time it is doing this, the moth lays an egg into this pollen ball. When the plant seeds have formed and the moth egg has hatched, the moth larva feeds on some of the seeds until it matures and is ready to transition into an adult moth.[7]

How two unlike organisms like a plant and an insect could be genetically programmed to be in such a relationship must be considered a miracle. Neither the plant nor the moth can survive without the other. The moth had to be genetically programmed to be attracted only by the flower of a yucca plant. The yucca plant had to be genetically programmed to receive pollen pushed into its carpel by the moth, because that is its only means of pollination.

The two genetic codes are programmed into the DNA of two independent organisms. This could be modeled as having two computer programs running on two different computers that have to interact with each other to produce two different products. In the computer world, this could happen only if both computer programs were designed by a single designer or by teams of designers who communicated every detail with each other. Only an Intelligent Designer programming both the plant DNA and, two days later, the insect DNA, can explain such a relationship.

As support of the CM-model, the mutual dependency of a plant and an animal to propagate their kind shows the intelligent design and planning capability of the Creator. These two organisms depend on each other but were made two days apart. The designs of the DNA in both would have had to include the dependency on the other from the beginning. Such a complex biological system design is far beyond the capability of any human to produce. Only the infinite knowledge of the Creator could design and build such a system. The designs had to be perfect at the start because they have continued for thousands of years.

SUMMARY

On the third day, God prepared the surface of planet Earth as the habitat for his living creatures. Most likely during the afternoon of that day, God caused live vegetation to sprout and cover the surface of the dry land and caused plant-like organisms to grow and prosper in the water, as shown in Illustration 6.4. The introduction of plant life to the surface habitat of Earth happened suddenly, at the same time, and everywhere on Earth. The author of the CMA indicated that not only did it happen suddenly, but also the plant ecosystem that resulted matured rapidly so that it was fully functional and complete. It was perfectly designed in every detail. No living organism, whether a single-celled bacterium or multi-celled plant, could have sustained itself without the multiple and complex chemical processes found in its cells. Any individual process by itself would have been of little benefit to a cell on its own.

ILLUSTRATION 6.4: Plants covering the land and
plant-like organisms growing in the water.

As a product of this miracle, the first living and reproducing cells were formed. We infer from scientific studies of plants that all the processes required by a cell to manufacture the carbohydrates, proteins, enzymes, genes, and chromosomes that are required for any plant to live were programmed into the DNA of the various plant cells. Scientific research has revealed that independent single-cell or multi-cell organisms, both on the land and in the seas, are optimally designed and made to support the ecosystem that was established. The ecosystem, in order to function properly, would have included plant-like organisms such as bacteria, fungi, and protists. These organisms support both plant and animal life.

The rapid maturing of plants to meet God's purpose is seen in the perfect design of their cells and their symbiotic relationships to the plant-like organisms. The growth rates required for the plants to mature in less than a day indicated that perfect and even accelerated chemical processes were required. Even with perfect internal processes, the growth rate of the plants could not have been sustained without their relationships to plant-like organisms such as bacteria and fungi.

The symbiotic relationships involving many of these living organisms have supplied overwhelming evidence that the ecosystem was designed and made by an Intelligent Designer and Creator. The habitat on the surface of the Earth was nearly prepared by the end of the third day for filling with God's living creatures—animals and mankind. At that time, it only lacked a continual source of energy that the plants require for growing and reproducing.

CHAPTER 7

Divine Action 6: Lighting and Fixing the Positions of the Luminaries

DAY 4: COMPLETING THE EXPANSE OF THE HEAVENS AND THEIR HOSTS

THE TWO PREVIOUS chapters described God's actions that prepared the surface of the planet now called Earth into the habitat in which his creatures would live. At the end of the third day, the surface of the planet was still missing one important item required for sustaining animal life. That item was a source of energy that would power the whole habitat and its ecosystems. The required source of energy was a star named Sol, commonly known as the sun.

At the beginning of the fourth day, God commanded lights to exist in the heavens. The purposes of these lights were to separate day and night; act as signs to help mankind determine months, days and years; and provide light and heat in the form of EMR to Earth. In the CM-model, celestial spheres called proto-stars had been dispersed into all the galaxies of the universe starting at dawn of the second day. We speculated that the spheres began as white-hot atomic matter and plasma ejected from white holes in the event horizon of ultra-massive black holes at the center of each galaxy. In the Milky Way galaxy (hereafter the galaxy), the solar system formed with its proto-planets and their spherical moons around its proto-star. The solar system had reached its final location in the galaxy sometime during the following two days, propelled by supernatural winds. On the way out from the white hole, the atomic matter on the surface of the proto-star had cooled down to a temperature so that it emitted minimal visible light. When its temperature reached that point, it had signaled the beginning (evening) of the third day.

All the events reported in the CMA for the third day described what took place on the planet Earth that was transformed into mankind's future habitat. We speculated that some natural processes may have continued in the remainder of the galaxy and the universe during the third day. For example, in the previous chapter we speculated that a beam of EMR and cosmic rays from the second white hole at the center of the galaxy rotated past the position of Earth to provide visible radiation and a bright aurora for the daylight period of the third day.

This source of daylight can be explained only if God was still supernaturally accelerating all the natural processes involved. For example, the velocity of light and all the atomic matter had to be much greater than that measured today on or near Earth. At the same time the white hole was the source of daylight, it also ejected the atomic matter that formed into celestial spheres in the second arm of star systems in the galaxy spiral. Similar events and process rates could have occurred in every galaxy in the universe during the third day on which the author of the CMA does not report.

On the fourth day, we infer that all God's actions in making the lights appear took place outside the atmosphere of Earth. This was emphasized by use of the phrase "in the expanse of the heavens" when referring to events happening on that day (Gen. 1:14–15,17). If mankind had been present, they would have seen from any location on the surface of Earth what was described in the five verses that report the products of God's divine actions.

How God made the stars shine and fixed their position in the sky can only be explained as more miracles. He ignited all the stars, including the sun, by starting their internal nuclear fusion and fission processes. The moon and the other planets of the solar system served as reflectors of the light that the sun provided. We speculate that the light from all other stars visible to the unaided eye also reached Earth on that day. These included the stars in the galaxy that had been placed so they formed constellations that could have been seen in the sky above Earth. These constellations are the signs God provided for mankind. Mankind have used these constellations to determine direction of travel and time of the year on Earth since ancient times.

It was significant that God left this great miracle until he had completed everything else on Earth. This delay in providing sunlight demonstrated again that his wondrous works of creation week included design and planning. Every ecosystem he had prepared on Earth before the fourth day could continue functioning only if energy was specifically supplied by the sun at the distance it is located from Earth. For example, there are many different types of stars but only the sun-type could optimally supply the visible light spectrum required by Earth and its new plant ecosystem. God had already placed Earth in its orbit around the sun so that it would receive the optimal amount of the energy needed to keep its surface water liquid. The miracle of providing the light from the sun and all the other celestial hosts of heaven again demonstrated his wondrous works for which all creation should praise him (Ps. 103:22).

OTHER BIBLICAL REFERENCES TO MIRACLE 6

Psalm 104:19–23

He made the moon for the seasons; the sun knows the place of its setting. You appoint darkness and it becomes night, in which all the beasts of the forest prowl about. The young lions roar after their prey and seek their food from God. When the sun rises they withdraw and lie down in their dens. Man goes forth to his work and to his labor until evening.
—Ps. 104:19–23

In these verses, the author alludes to God's purposes for making the sun and moon as lights in the sky on the fourth day. They were to provide light to the surface of Earth beginning on that day and divided daylight from nighttime. In verse 19a, the psalmist reported that one purpose for the moon was marking the passage of time called seasons. The Hebrew word translated *seasons* is defined as a set time period. In modern terms, this would be the period of time defined by phases of the moon that was called a month of the Hebrew calendar year. In ancient Hebrew times, the passing of three months or cycles of moon phases measured seasons of the year.

In the following verses, the author alludes to the purposes for the sun. The verses first picture the purpose for the absence of the sunlight at night. During that part of the day, the wild animals use the relative darkness to prowl about in search of food starting at the setting of the sun (vv. 19b–21). Next, the purpose for daylight is pictured. Wild animals retreat to their dens and mankind start their labor at the rising of the sun (vv. 22–23). These verses complement the purposes provided in verses 14–18 of the CMA for the sun and moon. There the author reported that the greater light (sun) should rule the day and the lesser light (moon) the night in providing light (including heat) to Earth.

Psalm 148:1–6

> *Praise the* LORD*! Praise the* LORD *from the heavens; praise Him in the heights! Praise Him, all His angels; praise Him, all His hosts! Praise Him, sun and moon; praise Him, all stars of light! Praise Him, highest heavens, and the waters that are above the heavens! Let them praise the name of the* LORD*, for He commanded and they were created. He has also established them forever and ever; He has made a decree which will not pass away.*
> —Ps. 148:1–6

This psalm is another song that urged all of God's creation to praise him. In verses 1–2, the author urged all the hosts of heaven (that included his spiritual hosts, the angels) to praise the Lord. In verse 3, the sun, moon, and stars, i.e., the hosts of the physical heavens, are urged to praise him. In verse 4, the author repeats this urging in parallel phrases to verses 1–3. He urges both the highest heavens, which may refer to the God's upper chambers (Ps. 104:3) and therefore includes the angels, and all the waters (original fluid matter) that were separated above in the expanse to praise him. According to the CM-model, this fluid matter had been transformed into all the celestial spheres or hosts of the physical heavens on the second day.

The NASB translation renders the literal Hebrew phrase "heaven of the heavens" in verse 4 as the "highest heavens." An alternate translation that could have been used is the phrase "the expanse of the heavens" as was used in the CMA (Gen. 1:14–18). This would have emphasized that God named the expanse *heavens* in Genesis 1:8 after making it.

Divine Action 6: Lighting and Fixing the Positions of the Luminaries

In this case verse 4 would be parallel to verse 3 alone and refer to the physical heavens and hosts. But in verse 5, the author states: "For He commanded and they were created," which would include both spiritual and physical heavens and their hosts as in verse 1.

The Hebrew phrase in verse 6 rendered "forever and ever" by this translation normally referred to an indeterminate period of time in the future. When God promised to end time in the future, he also promised to make the physical heavens pass away (Mark 13:26–31).

1 Corinthians 15:41

> *There is one glory of the sun, and another glory of the moon, and another glory of the stars; for star differs from star in glory.*
>
> —1 Cor. 15:41

This verse emphasizes the difference between the sun, moon, and stars in radiance or brightness. It points out that there is a difference between one star and another. This difference in light output was dependent on the physical characteristics of each star, such as their size and the atomic elements they contained. The atomic elements that emit light at the surface of the star determine the output color of the light. Another reason some stars appear brighter than others is the presence of more than one star in a stellar system. At sufficient distance, several stars can appear as a single source.

More General References

Other Bible references to the lighting of the luminaries, their location in the expanse, and their purposes, can be found in Deuteronomy 4:19; Job 9:9, 37:18, 38:31–33; Psalm 8:3, 33:6, 74:16–17, 136:7–9, 147:4; and Jeremiah 31:35. In 2 Peter 3:7 the author reports that God has reserved the heavens, including the stars he made, for fire at the end of time. Also, in Luke 21:25–27 the author reports that the sun, moon, and stars will signal that the last day has arrived. These references all confirm the purposes for the stars and constellations as observed by mankind from the surface of Earth as stated in CMA verse 18. They serve as light providers at night, signs for mankind to determine location and direction on Earth's surface, and a means to mark the passage of time. In Genesis 1:14 the author states that God established them all on the fourth day to fulfill these purposes.

SCIENTIFIC TERMINOLOGY

Star Types

Many different types of stars are observed in the universe. The majority of the visible stars are called *main-sequence* stars. They vary in color and size ranging from the blue-white stars the size of the sun to giant red stars the size of Earth's orbit around the sun. Astronomers assume all of these stars have the same structure as shown in the cut-away drawing of the sun in Illustration 7.1. The main-sequence designation was applied to the stars by astronomers who believe that stars evolve from one type to the next in a sequence based on size and color. For example, according to their theory, the sun evolved from a smaller blue-white star to its present size and color in the past 5 billion years. They also claim that as the sun continues to evolve, it will grow into a red giant. This evolutionary growth of the sun is predicted to occur over the next 5 billion years, and by that time it will envelop Earth. These claims are based on the Big Bang theory of the evolution of the universe. A more detailed description of the main sequence is provided later in the CM-model paragraphs. All that astronomers have found by observations is that surface temperature and the atomic elements that radiate their light determine the color and radiance of stars. They have never observed a star that changed from one type to another while evolving according to the main sequence.

There are some other types of stars that are not considered stars of the main sequence. For example, dark-red-to-brown dwarf stars are considered failed stars because they never had enough gravity to sustain the basic nuclear processes found in all the larger stars for a long period of time. Their size is estimated to be only 25 to 80 times the size of the planet Jupiter or less than 0.2 the size of the sun. They essentially became large gas giant planets that mainly emitted infrared and microwave radiation. But astronomers have found them in binary star systems with main-sequence partners, and others have been found with orbiting planets. Two other types of stars, the white dwarf stars and the neutron stars, are considered products of a supernova that occurred in a larger main-sequence star. The origin of these stars is described in more detail in the following supernova paragraphs.

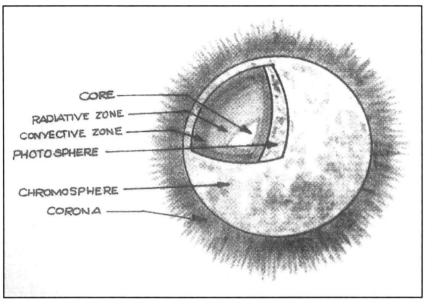

ILLUSTRATION 7.1: A cutaway drawing that shows the internal structure of the sun.

Supernova

A star that implodes while it gives off a gigantic burst of EMR and atomic particles causes a supernova. The star implodes (collapsed into a smaller object) because its gravity becomes stronger than the pressure its light-generating nuclear processes can produce. This implosion occurs when the star has used up the nuclear fuel (mostly hydrogen) that produces its light. It is considered the end of life for that star. Very large stars that collapse become black holes, while medium-sized stars become neutron stars. Small stars, the size of the sun and up to eight times larger, implode to form white dwarfs, and the atomic particles that they emit form their surrounding nebulas.

A special supernova called Type 1a is observed only in theory when the star that implodes is a member of a binary star system. The imploding star started out as a star that was too small and did not have sufficient gravity to implode. At that stage it was a white dwarf that was formed by a supernova of a red giant. But because it was in a binary system, it was able to extract enough gas from the companion star to reach the size and mass for another implosion threshold. A binary star system with a large and a small star exchanging plasma is shown in Illustration 7.2. Theoretically, when it implodes, the amount of EMR released would be the same as every other Type 1a event. The Type 1a supernova is now being used as a standard light source to measure the large distances to other galaxies in the universe. The result of this type of supernova is a neutron star in a binary system with a main-sequence star.

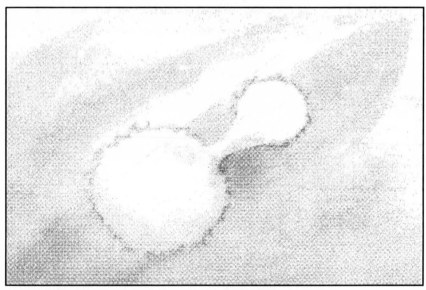

ILLUSTRATION 7.2: A binary star system before it becomes a Type 1a supernova.

Constellations

Constellations are made up of single and multiple star systems in a formation within the galaxy. Stars outside the galaxy were not made part of constellations because they are not visible to the unaided eye. The only two galaxies outside the galaxy that are visible to the unaided eye are not considered part of any constellation by observers, because they appear too dim and fuzzy to be a star. The constellations Job wrote about in Job 9:9, approximately four thousand years ago, have remained recognizable to this day. It can be inferred from their retention of their overall shape that the universe was designed and built so that the stars or star clusters within a constellation do not change significantly in relative position to each other.

Time Dilation

Time dilation is the term given to the change in a time interval, such as a second, as the force of gravity at a location is increased. In simple terms, if a clock approached a source of gravity like Earth from outer space, the time interval that it measured as a second would increase. Time would slow down as gravity increased and would speed up when it decreased. Near large massive objects there is "slower time" and in deep space away from galaxies and stars there is "faster time." Clocks that have been placed in orbit around Earth have measured this effect. An extreme example of time dilation should be observed if a clock approached a black hole. Theoretically, when a clock reached the event horizon, the second would be so long it would appear that time has stopped and the clock was not changing.

Distances to Other Galaxies

One theory that is used to make distance estimates to other galaxies is based on the fact that, if a known amount of light (energy) is emitted by a source, the amount of light received at different distances from that source can be calculated. The amount of light emitted by a supernova Type 1a event has been theoretically calculated based on assumptions of what caused the implosion. Distances to them are then calculated based on the amount of light received on Earth. This measurement technique is called the Luminosity-Distance (LD) method. These distances have been compared with those from results of other measurement methods. For example, distances obtained from measuring the redshift of a galaxy that contained a supernova have been consistent for many Type 1a supernovas. Where possible, these two methods are used to verify the results of one by the other.

THE CM-MODEL

Our development of the CM-model describing the heavens ended with a possible source for daylight on the third day for Earth's newly formed surface. We speculated that this light source was a result of processes that may have taken place in space above Earth's atmosphere. The proposed cosmic source of daylight was therefore incidental to making the atmosphere transparent by burning dark particles and gases. It allowed the visible light caused by a beam of EMR and cosmic particles from a second white hole at the center of the galaxy as it rotated past Earth's position to reach the surface. We assumed that the sprouting of all the vegetation and the formation of the entire plant ecosystem took place during this period of daylight. The CMA began the fourth day with a description of what God did in the expanse of the heavens to provide mankind with a perpetual source of EMR for heat and light and a wondrous display of the hosts he had placed there.

Divine Act 6

Let there be lights in the expanse of the heavens to separate the day from the night, and let them be for signs and for seasons and for days and years; and let them provide light on the earth.
—Gen. 1:14–15, paraphrased

The lighting of the proto-stars was the miracle that began the fourth day. God would also fix their locations in the sky by the end of the day. These lights included both the light providers and the light reflectors that are distributed throughout space above Earth. We have inferred from Psalms 104:3 and 148:4–6 that the material from which God had made these proto-stars and reflectors was the fluidic matter called the "waters above" in the CMA (Gen. 1:7) that had been dispersed throughout the universe.

According to the CM-model, these fluids had been separated first by being formed into dark clouds that we called black holes. God then supernaturally dispersed the black holes containing the fluids throughout the universe to locations at least close to where all the galaxies now exist. Then the black holes developed openings in their event horizons that we called white holes. These white holes ejected the atomic matter that formed the galaxies of celestial spheres. These spheres were the proto-stars, proto-planets, and spherical moons that populated the universe as the hosts of the physical heavens. Besides the celestial spheres, the galaxies also included clouds of gas, dust, and asteroids that may lie inside or outside the stellar systems.

Stars and Sun Formation

One major result of Divine Act 6 was the transformation of the proto-stars into light providers. We speculated that the proto-stars had formed quickly into spheres of compressed gas (or possibly liquid at some point within their structure) after their departure from the white hole. By the time they had reached their locations in their galaxies, they were fully formed into spheres, but their surfaces had cooled to temperatures that prevented them from giving off more than a small amount of visible light. God did not establish their internal processes that made them light providers until the fourth day.

In contrast to terrestrial planets like Earth, the transformation that took place on the proto-stars occurred deep inside and not only on their surface. The temperature near the center of the sun is estimated to be 15 million Kelvins. This temperature is required to sustain the nuclear fusion process that transforms hydrogen into helium and other elements. It is estimated that the energy produced in the central core of the sun takes a long time to be conducted to the surface from 700,000 kilometers (420,000 miles) below. At natural process rates, it would take millions of years for this energy to reach the surface where it is emitted as light and heat.

In the CM-model, the internal processes originated with hot gases or liquid already present within the star or sun from when it was ejected by the white hole and formed a sphere. The cooling process that took place during the trip to its location in the galaxy occurred mainly on or near its surface. We speculate that the cooling of the surface kept the sun from shining on the third day. It was even possible that God commanded the sun and stars not to shine on the third day as can be inferred from Job 9:7: "Who commands the sun not to shine, And sets a seal upon the stars." On the fourth day, God's command to the proto-stars to light up established the natural processes now taking place within the sun and the other stars. We speculate that this ignition occurred at supernaturally accelerated rates. The stars immediately became continuous heat and light providers as most of them still are today.

We infer from verse 14 of the CMA that most, if not all, of the proto-stars in the universe responded to God's command at the same time. For the CM-model, this took place at the beginning of the fourth day. Previously, the beginning of a day had been defined as the evening and not the beginning of daylight. However, the lighting of the sun at the start of the fourth day brought a new viewpoint to the definition of a day.

The fourth day and all those following it are defined relative to a specific location on Earth's surface. The evening of the fourth day still took place first at one location on Earth as the day was defined in verse 5 of the CMA. But it was morning at a location on the opposite side of Earth that was rotating to face the sun. It was also in the report of this day's events that the CMA first provided enough information to determine the duration of a day that God had defined four days earlier. We infer from Genesis 1:16–17 that the length of a day was one rotation of Earth on its axis, which takes approximately twenty-four hours. This time standard, plus the standards for a month and year, are shown in Illustration 7.3.

For the CM-model, it made no difference where on Earth it was daylight or nighttime when God commanded the sun to first provide its light. The standard for the daily cycle was established at that moment for any specific location on Earth's surface. In equatorial zones, the twenty-four hours is evenly divided between nighttime and daylight. In regions near the poles, there are both twenty-four hours of daylight or nighttime depending on the season of the year. We infer from the CMA that God had set the rotation rate of Earth to fit the standard day he had defined on the first day (Gen. 1:5).

A new standard for separation of light (day) and darkness (night) was also established as the author of the CMA reported in the parallel verses 14 and 18. The separation line or terminator formed where Earth shielded half its surface from the light of the sun as described in Proverbs 8:27, "When He inscribed a circle on the face of the deep." This illustrated the dependence of the time of day on the position of the sun at any one surface location. The permanent establishment of this time standard was confirmed by other Biblical references to the results of this miracle, such as Psalm 74:16–17, 104:19–23, 136:7–9; and Jeremiah 31:35.

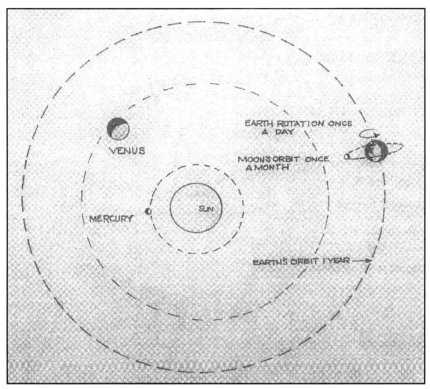

ILLUSTRATION 7.3: The time standards as determined from the sun, Earth, and moon.

Appearance of the Stars' Ages

Mankind have observed the stars for as long as they have existed. Most dedicated observers have noticed that some stars are brighter than others, differ in color, and even change brightness and/or color with time. Modern astronomers have constructed a system by which they claim that they can tell the age of a star by determining its brightness and color. For a general description of that system, called the Hertzsprung-Russell (H-R) diagram, see DeYoung's book or any introductory astronomy textbook.[1] The Bible reports that luminaries differ in glory (1 Cor. 15:41). This verse most likely refers to the heavenly hosts' observable differences in brightness and color. We infer for the CM-model that God made all the different stars in such a way that their unique light began to shine on the fourth day, not after millions of years of development. We infer from Psalm 147:4 that God controlled the total number of stars and the formation of each individual star as he gave them their names.

The brightness differences between stars can be explained as a combination of their surface atomic elements and their temperature, their distance from Earth, and whether each is a single star or a multiple star system. The majority of visible stars are made up of at least two stars orbiting each other in a binary star system. Astronomers have observed other star systems that have three or four stars that orbit each other. The eclipsing of one of the two stars in a binary system by the other causes one type of variability in brightness and color of a star. The brightness and color vary the most when there is a large difference in brightness and/or color between the individual stars in the system.

Most of the stars that are visible to the unaided eye can be considered main-sequence stars. Stars like the sun that are yellow are located in the middle of the color range. The total wavelength range of stars that has been observed through telescopes is extended beyond the visible to both shorter and longer wavelengths. This range includes everything from invisible neutron stars that emit x-rays to the smallest brown dwarf stars—not much larger than a gas giant planet—that mainly emit wavelengths much longer than those that are visible.

The apparent age of stars using the H-R diagram was determined indirectly from their brightness and color. The method the astronomers used is greatly dependent on the assumption that stars develop from one type to the next over a long period of time, changing their temperature and the atomic-element fuel used in their nuclear processes. Computer models have been built to explain all the variations in the stars of the main sequence based on known nuclear processes that could be occurring in them. These efforts have led astronomers to also categorize stars into a sequence of three generations according to their perceived stage of development. But examples of a first-generation star have never been observed due to their supposedly short lifetime close to the beginning of the universe that allegedly occurred billions of years ago.

Divine Action 6: Lighting and Fixing the Positions of the Luminaries

Based on the Bible's account of history, the long time periods required for the development and aging of stars have not occurred. A creation model therefore must explain the large variety of stars both in brightness and color without dependence on the assumption of stars developing over a long period of time from one type to another. All the star types provided their unique light on the fourth day when they were converted from the proto-stars that had been formed in the previous two days.

Star Formation in the CM-Model

The initial formation of the proto-stars was modeled previously in connection with Divine Act 3. The CM-model included our speculation that the process of nucleosynthesis formed all the atomic elements when the atomic matter was still inside the ultra-massive black holes at the center of the galaxies. Therefore, all atomic elements would naturally be represented to some extent in the fluid matter that exited the white holes and formed the celestial spheres. The amount of each atomic element in the composition of a proto-star depended on when and where it exited from the white hole. The amount of fluid available in the proto-star's neighborhood as it formed into a sphere determines the size of the proto-star.

Surface temperature mainly determines the color and brightness of a star. The surface temperature depends heavily on the nuclear processes that produce the electromagnetic energy within the star. The gravitational-field strength that is determined by a star's size and composition plays a major role in the rates of these nuclear processes. Ultimately, it is only the size and composition of each star that actually determines both brightness and color of its light. Therefore God could have given stars their unique characteristics when he completed them on the fourth day. The differences between stars due to their age and development from one type to another according to the H-R diagram can be considered only a theory constructed to support the long ages of the evolution of the universe.

Starlight Travel Time and the Speed of Light

We infer from the CMA that starlight from stars visible to the unaided human eye reached the surface of Earth on the same day that the stars started shining. These stars would have been the ones found in the constellations that are still visible in the night sky. Due to physical limitations on their size and brightness, all the stars that are visible to the human eye have to be located within a distance of approximately 6,000 light years from Earth. Measurements of the distance to the stars found in the constellations have confirmed that they are all in a small spherical portion of the galaxy with that radius centered on Earth. But even 6,000 lys was more than 2 million times as far as light could have traveled in one day at its presently measured speed on or near Earth.

Most scientists have assumed that light has always traveled at a constant speed throughout the whole universe. If that were true, light could not have arrived on Earth the fourth day from stars at a distance greater than approximately 0.003 ly. The distance to the nearest visible star has been measured to be more than 4 lys. If the assumption of a constant light speed were correct, that would imply there was no starlight on Earth for at least four years and no constellations would have been visible until thousands of years after the stars started to shine. This conclusion, of course, supports the long time periods that most scientists have built into the models of the evolution of the universe.

For the CM-model, we speculate that the processes that took place on the fourth day occurred at a rate that would not be considered normal on Earth today. We pointed out in previous chapters describing the first three days that on the first day, the original fluid blob expanded rapidly as light and atomic matter formed. On the second day, the black holes carrying the fluids were moved at supernatural speeds, the celestial spheres in the galaxies traveled thousands of light years to their locations in the galaxies, and their surfaces cooled in less than twelve hours. On the third day, Earth's oceans, landmasses, and atmosphere formed in less than a single day. Even plants grew to their full height and maturity to provide seeds and fruit in less than a day. All these examples point to fast time that would support superluminal speed for both energy (light) and atomic matter. All the other natural processes would also have had proportionately higher rates.

Light speed also has been found to change with distance from a source of gravity. We explained in an earlier chapter that the speed of a particle is measured by how fast it changes position. If the time interval used to measure the speed of a particle's motion changes, then the resultant measurement would also be expected to change. This effect of gravity on photons would be difficult to measure because the speed of light is the fastest of all particle motions, and gravity is the weakest force. The combination of these two factors has made the measurement of the change in the speed of light in a changing gravitational field impossible within the solar system. But the solar system has been the only place where mankind are able to make such a measurement.

A Solution to the Starlight-Travel-Time Dilemma for a Young Universe

Young-Earth creation scientists have proposed two solutions to the dilemma of starlight travel time and its arrival on Earth on the fourth day, considering the long distances to all the stars. Barry Setterfield has proposed that light had a greater speed at the beginning of creation and has been slowing down ever since.[2] Russ Humphreys has used time dilation to explain how processes happened much faster at the outer reaches of the universe where gravity would be much less compared to the vicinity of Earth.[3] A close look at these two models reveals that they have a common element. That common element is smaller time intervals or fast time. Light would travel the same distance in the smaller interval and therefore faster. This would be taking place in space where there was a lower-strength gravitational field. In other words, the rate of all natural processes, including light speed, could have been higher in a smaller gravitational field relative to their rate in a location with greater gravity, as on the surface of Earth that is near the center of the universe. The speed of both energy and matter in 4-D space-time would have been dependent on the gravitational field they are passing through. One result would have been that the speed of light between star systems and galaxies where gravity is much less may have been much greater than the speed of light as measured on Earth.

How This Solution Fits Creation Week

The problem of starlight arriving on Earth within one day from all stars visible to the human eye can be solved with an average increase of light speed by two million times its speed on Earth. This increase could have been possible on the fourth day within the galaxy in the local region where all the stars of the constellations are located (i.e., the 6000 ly sphere centered on Earth). Beyond this local region along the distance toward the center of the galaxy, the gravity would increase so that time and light speed would slow down. In a direction out of the galaxy, the time intervals would have decreased as gravity continued to decrease and the speed of light would have increased even more. We speculate that God could have controlled time to make process rates speed up just as he controlled energy and matter during creation week. What remains uncertain is whether space warping and time dilation are permanently built into the universe. God may have terminated these effects by the end of the fourth day of creation week.

The CMA and therefore the CM-model has described God setting up the structure of the universe and the physical laws that will govern it for all time during the first four days of creation. In that time period, there would have been no natural limits to the rate of any processes that occurred. Once God introduced animals on the fifth day, any motion, at least on Earth, needed to be limited to what animals are designed to comprehend and their bodies could sustain.

The question may never be answered as to whether God built fast and slow time into the final product so that they still exist somewhere at far distances from Earth today. Mankind's small reach into outer space with robotic spacecraft has not even extended beyond the solar system. Most scientists have ignored the possibility of a varying relationship between gravity, light, and space-time, because it would have contradicted one of their major theories concerning the origins of the universe. They have built into the Big Bang model their belief in the natural evolution of the universe. How God actually created the universe is an area of research that remains wide open for young-Earth creation scientists who believe what he has recorded for them in the CMA.

Redshift of Light and Distance to Stars

Edwin Hubble discovered the observed relationship between redshift of light and distance to a galaxy in the 1920s. His initial observations and the data he collected on galaxies were the first to establish that there are galaxies beyond the Milky Way galaxy. Then he went on to show that the brighter galaxies were not as red as the dimmer galaxies. He further determined that the brighter galaxies were closer to Earth than the dimmer galaxies that contained greater redshifted spectral lines.

Hubble formalized this relationship in what is called Hubble's law. It related the reddening, or the shift to longer wavelengths of the spectral lines emitted by a galaxy, to the galaxy's distance from Earth. The Redshift-Distance (RSD) method was calibrated by comparing the resulting distances to the Luminosity-Distance (LD) measurements described earlier. The consistency of results from these two measurement methods for distance to a galaxy is well documented. A third method called Angular Diameter-Distance (ADD) has also shown distance measurement results that are consistent with RSD for galaxies closer to Earth where ADD can be used.

Astronomers explain the redshift relationship to distance between galaxies by what is called the Hubble flow. However, the Hubble flow has not been directly detected and remains only theoretical. It was based on assumptions, because it is impossible to travel to another galaxy to make any direct measurement. The main assumptions are that light speed in a vacuum remains a constant everywhere and that all natural processes take place at the same rate throughout the universe.

According to the evolutionary Standard Theory, the expansion of space itself during the time light traveled from a distant galaxy to Earth caused the Hubble flow redshift. The expansion of space supposedly stretched the light waves to longer wavelengths, causing the light to redden. Neither the expansion of space nor the force it exerted on light to stretch the wavelength has ever been detected or demonstrated. It was proposed as an explanation of RSD that supported the Big Bang model of evolutionary development of the universe. For a more comprehensive description of the expansion of space and Hubble flow see Faulkner's book *Universe by Design*.[4]

RSD and Creation

For scientists who support a recent creation, the CMA made the statement that the stars were made light sources in their relative locations on the fourth day (Gen. 1:16–17) to provide light to Earth.

We infer from what can be observed that all galaxies were also fixed in their locations on that day. We speculate that the CM-model can be extended to explain the RSD relationship. The speculation is that the measured redshift occurred during a single twenty-four-hour day of fast time. This occurred before God fixed the location of stars and galaxies at the end of the fourth day. In simple terms, what observers have reported as million or billion years of development occurred all in one day of fast time. The observed process rates of the events on that day were slowed by millions or billions of times in the light that is received on Earth. This slowing is caused by time dilation and space warping between the galaxies and Earth. It is like a movie made in regular time and played back in slow motion. This effect can also be used to explain any development of stars from one type to the next such as a neutron star formed in an event like a supernova. These events also took place at different times on the fourth day.

Instead of just unexplainable space expansion along the path light traveled to Earth, the 4-D space-time was supernaturally warped on the fourth day. This warping effect involved both space and time, both of which are directly related to light speed and gravity. Whether it was the spatial distance or the size of the intervals of time that changed along the path cannot be determined from a measurement made on light arriving on Earth. If time dilation occurred, the observed redshift could be the well-understood Doppler shifting, described in a previous chapter, due to a galaxy's motion away from the observer here on Earth and not due to Hubble flow. Within the galaxy, the only detectable redshifted or blueshifted light from stars is due to their regular Doppler motion relative to Earth. Theoretically, the Hubble flow can only be detected at the great distances that lie between galaxies.

The CM-model as just described has superluminal speeds and accelerated process rates still taking place on the fourth day after the stars started shining. Then time dilation and space warping combined to present a slow-motion picture of a galaxy on that day to Earth. The light bringing the information started out at a greatly increased speed and slowed as it traveled toward the center of the universe. It slowed further as it entered the gravity of the galaxy and then the solar system. Astronomers have therefore observed the accelerated or fast time processes by the light that has slowed down to its present speed on Earth. If the speed of light slowed, then the process rates of events observed would also appear slowed to their normal rates on Earth. A day of accelerated process rates of events in fast time would look like millions or billions of days of the normal process rate of events in slow time on Earth. The events such as supernova, gamma ray bursts, and pulsars would appear at the same rates as if they were taking place nearby in the galaxy and not billions of light years away.

Their motion away from Earth at superluminal speeds would cause the redshift of spectral lines from any galaxy or quasar during a very short fast-time period on the fourth day of creation. Because the redshift is related to the distance from Earth, the galaxies could have been moving away at different rates, depending on that distance. The light that reached Earth carried the original Doppler-shift information of the source's accelerated motion but presented it in slow motion to the observer in his slower time.

Permanent Constellations

The author of the CMA reported that God placed the luminaries in the sky in their relative locations with respect to each other to form recognizable signs (v. 14). Other references from the Bible, such as Job 9:9, 37:18, 38:31–33, and Psalm 8:3 confirm that this report applied to the stars in the constellations visible to the human eye from Earth's surface. In simple terms, the stars have not moved away from or towards each other by an amount that is detectable by an unaided observer on Earth. They are essentially fixed in their relative position in the sky. As described in a paragraph above, all the stars in visible constellations are located within the galaxy in a sphere centered on Earth and orbit around the center of the galaxy as more or less a unit.

We infer from the relatively fixed positions of the stars that God specially constructed the galaxy so the stars would permanently stay in their constellations. He first distributed the stars after they exited through the white holes to fit into their constellations in the designed spiral pattern of the galaxy. At the same time, he made the gravity of the individual stars to form the gravitational field that supports the galaxy structure. For the CM-model, we speculate that God formed the galaxy as an island in space so that it is nearly independent from any other galaxy. Its gravitational field has shaped the space-time dimensions within its boundaries so that the stars in its disk orbit the center bulge at a nearly constant linear velocity.

In a previous chapter, we speculated that the galaxy formed quickly and therefore in fast time. But after its formation was completed with the lighting of the stars, we infer that God slowed time and all process rates to their present values, especially near Earth. According to the CMA, by the end of the fourth day the heavens were completed with all the stars shining and fixed in their locations (Gen 1:17–18). The galaxy with its stars had become the permanent light provider to Earth, and its stars were fixed in their relative locations to provide signs for mankind to observe until the end of time.

SCIENTIFIC EVIDENCE THAT SUPPORTS THE CM-MODEL

Scientific evidence supports four portions of this latest extension to the CM-model. Astronomers have made several observations that have not been easy to fit into the evolutionary theory of the Big Bang model but fit much better into the CM-model. To force this observational data to fit the Big Bang model, some scientists have used their imagination and have added patches to the original Standard Theory of the evolution of the universe. They have suggested the accelerating expansion of space, an undetected form of matter called "dark matter," and a mysterious anti-gravity force that no one knows anything about that they have labeled "dark energy." They have taken these extreme measures to support their theory, but instead the need for these patches may indicate that their theory is not correct.

The CM-model can explain at least certain of these observations without resorting to such extreme measures. The observations that it can explain include: a) the apparent slowing down of the two Pioneer spacecraft at a faster rate than predicted by Newton's (or Einstein's) law of gravity; b) stars on the outer edge of the galaxy are moving at a velocity that cannot be explained by Kepler's laws of orbital motion; c) galaxies are located in spherical shells at discrete distances from Earth, as measured by their quantized redshifts; and d) light from distant galaxies and quasars are focused on Earth by gravity lenses that are formed by galaxies and clusters of galaxies located in front of them.

Pioneer Spacecraft Slowing Down Faster Than Expected

Two Pioneer spacecraft (numbers 10 and 11) were sent to take pictures and collect other data on a flyby of the planet Jupiter and transmit them back to Earth. After completing their planetary observations, they were redirected into paths that would eventually take them out of the solar system in opposite directions. In 1980, they had passed the orbit of Uranus and had reached a distance from the sun where the sun's radiation wind no longer pushed them enough to affect their speed. At this time, it became possible to measure their slow-down rate due only to the attraction of solar system gravity. The National Aeronautics and Space Administration (NASA) scientists kept in contact with the spacecraft to obtain data about the space environment in which they were flying for as long as possible. The data collection continued until their transmitters stopped sending in 1990 (Pioneer 11) and 1998 (Pioneer 10). The distance to the spacecraft was constantly measured by the Doppler shift in the frequency of their radio transmissions.

Analysis of the collected data showed that the distance measured to the spacecraft did not match the distance scientists calculated using Newton's law of gravity.[5] The difference indicated a constant deceleration that could not be explained. NASA scientists have analyzed the data over a period of nine years and have officially acknowledged that they do not have a solution for this discrepancy.

Several creation models have attempted to explain this anomalous deceleration. Humphreys gave a detailed analysis of the deceleration with his model.[6] In that article, he described the cause of the effect as a reduction in gravity related to the distance from the center of the universe that he proposed would be located somewhere within the solar system.

Another possible solution along this same line of reasoning is offered here to explain the deceleration. In this solution, the decrease in gravity as the spacecraft leaves the solar system causes time intervals at the spacecraft to shorten. This time dilation would have increased the speed of the radio waves (also a form of EMR) and the process rates in the spacecraft as the spacecraft transmitters left the center of the solar system. This would reduce the Doppler shift measured back on Earth. A smaller value for the Doppler shift translates into a smaller distance measured to the spacecraft. The concept of light speed increasing in lower gravity to what is considered a superluminal speed had not been taken into account in any previous analysis. The scientists assumed that light speed was constant everywhere in the universe and cannot increase beyond the value measured in a vacuum on Earth.

The Galaxy Rotation

We inferred from the CMA that God constructed the constellations visible to the unaided eye so that their stars remained fixed in location relative to each other. As explained earlier, these stars are all located in a local spherical region of the galaxy. In physical terms, all the stars in a constellation have orbited around the center of the galaxy more or less as a unit since they were fixed in their orbits. This implies that the stars in a constellation were left orbiting the galaxy center with nearly the same velocity at the end of the fourth day.

What astronomers have discovered by observing the red shift of many stars in the galaxy and the orbiting of stars in other galaxies supports this concept. An article by Worraker contains a review of the astronomical studies of the early 1980s that describe this relationship.[7]

Comparing an orbital motion of the stars to the orbiting planets in the solar system can explain the difficulty in understanding such an unexpected orbital motion of the stars. The planets in the solar system orbit around the sun at different velocities, depending on their distance from it. For example, while Earth orbits the sun in approximately 365 days, it takes Mars 690 days to make one orbit because Mars has a longer distance to travel and travels at a slower velocity. The solar-system planets simply follow Newton's law of gravity that predicts the farther away a planet is from the sun, the slower it should travel in its orbit. Therefore, Mercury orbits at a velocity of about 48 km/s, Earth at 30 km/s, and Pluto, a dwarf planet on the outer fringe of the solar system, at 4.7 km/s. From the observations of the stars in the galaxy, astronomers have determined that they do not follow this supposedly universal law of orbital motion. Astronomers have found the stars near the edge of the galaxy travel as fast, or even faster, than the stars closer to the central bulge.

Scientists have attempted to explain this discrepancy by introducing enough dark matter into the galaxy until, with the additional gravity, the visible stars orbit as they have been observed. But they have not directly detected this dark matter nor have they explained where it came from or why it is located to cause the desired effect. They have determined that their model would require at least five to ten times the amount of dark matter mass as all the mass contained by the visible stars. It is difficult for them to explain why all that dark matter remains hidden unless it was made of some undetectable exotic matter that interacts only by gravity. Dark matter has not yet been shown to exist.

The CM-model posits that God determined the orbital velocity of the stars around the center of the galaxy when he made them and placed them in their relative positions. He originally formed the spiral galaxy as an island in space by having its stars spiral out of a central black hole. He moved each star system to its location in the galaxy with supernatural winds. Once the stars were in position, he stopped the spiral formation and set the final rotation rate of the galaxy and therefore the orbital velocity of all its stars.

The permanent location of the visible stars in their constellations was one of God's great miracles reported in the CMA and confirmed in Isaiah 51:16. We infer from Psalm 119:89–91 that God established the physical laws that govern all space, time, and matter in the universe when he formed the physical heavens. He also designed them so that they are preserved until the end of time. By requiring a natural explanation, scientists who support evolution have placed their belief in the existence of an unknown substance called dark matter as their alternative to belief in the Creator.

Quantized Redshift

The observation that galaxies are found in spherical shells at discrete distances around the solar system and Earth is not popular among scientists who support evolution. This observation implies that Earth is at least near to the center of the visible universe. A review of the observations that support quantized redshifts can be found in Humphreys' article.[8]

According to the Standard Theory and Big Bang model, everyplace in the universe should have an identical view of the universe. This theory was based on an infinite universe and does not allow for a center or even an edge to the universe. A recent patch to the theory requires dark energy's continual acceleration of the expansion of the universe. Such universal expansion does not allow for quantized redshifts. Many scientists have attempted to minimize the disruptive effect of quantized redshifts by claiming that the effect results from a faulty statistical analysis of a small data sample. However, the more the data sample has increased in size since the initial results were published, the more visible the effect has become.

We speculated for the CM-model that God distributed the galaxies out from the original point of creation of the material from which they were formed. In simple terms, he started with a blob of primordial earth (a fluid or "waters") at the center of the universe. We speculate that he could have arranged the galaxies in shells around this center as the quantized redshift data implies. He was forming the universe for mankind, so the design could have included structure that would only be viewed from man's perspective. Such structure in the universe would have demonstrated again the great order and complexity God designed and built into his created habitat for mankind.

Gravity Lenses

The observation of gravity lenses gives more support for time dilation and the slowing of light. Gravity lenses are formed by gravitational fields around large concentrations of masses, such as a large galaxy or a tight cluster of galaxies. Each gravity lens focuses light from sources such as other galaxies or quasars located beyond it. The image is magnified so that one can observe sources at great distances that would not be directly visible. Astronomers have used this effect to look at the farthest galaxies that have so far been detected. They have claimed that they are looking at galaxies formed within 500 million years after the Big Bang or at a distance of over 13 billion lys. Of course, those claims are based on assumptions that may be false, and therefore the distances they assume to these objects may not be accurate.

Divine Action 6: Lighting and Fixing the Positions of the Luminaries

Light passing through a simple glass lens is focused because glass has an index of refraction that is different from the air around it. The index of refraction of the glass slows the light wave as it passes through the lens. In a simple focusing lens that is thin at the edge and gets thicker toward the center, the speed of the wave changes so light that passes anywhere through the lens reaches the focal point of the lens at the same time. In other words, the light near the edge is slowed less and bent more toward the focus than the light that follows a line through the center of the lens. The light from the edges meets the light passing through the center at the focus of the lens, and together they form a magnified image.

A gravity lens cannot be considered a simple lens, but it must have a similar effect on light to obtain focusing and magnification. Instead of an index of refraction like glass has, the distribution of gravity within the galaxy lens acts as the medium that bends and slows the light wave passing through it. Gravity is reduced as the distance from the concentrated mass in the galaxy is increased. Therefore light waves passing farther from the edge slow less and bend more than those passing closer to or through the galaxy. A glass spherical lens is known to distort the image and sometimes form more than one image of a source. These effects are similar to those in the images observed through a gravity lens. That type of a distortion in an observed image of a quasar first led to the discovery of a gravity lens.

Bright sources, like quasars, are found widely spread throughout the universe, and no two have been found that are exactly alike. In 1979, scientists observed two apparently identical quasars that had the same redshift and were in close proximity to each other. An investigation showed that the "two" quasars were two images of a single quasar that was located beyond the galaxy cluster. This dual image effect is shown in Illustration 7.4. For a general review of gravity lenses, see the article by Koopmans and Blandford.[9]

The change in direction of starlight passing by the sun first demonstrated the effect that gravity has on light. But when Einstein first proposed his theory of gravity (general relativity) that explained this effect, he based it on the assumption that the speed of light was always a constant everywhere. He then explained the change of direction in the path of the starlight passing near the sun as the warping of space-time by gravity and the light path followed the curvature caused by this warp. We proposed for the CM-model that during creation week, God controlled both space and time. One major result we have highlighted was a change of the speed of light due to changes in gravity.

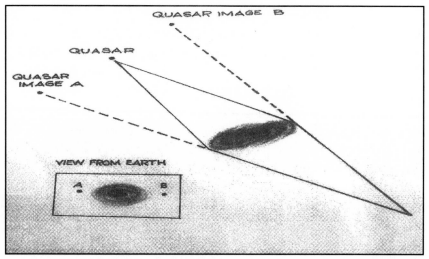

ILLUSTRATION 7.4: Two images of the same quasar due to a galaxy gravity lens.

We propose that the combination of light slowing down from superluminal speeds and space-time warping leads to an explanation for a gravity lens. There is no need to add dark matter to increase the gravity in galaxies and galaxy clusters as most astronomers have done. In the CM-model, the light wave that starts from a quasar source is traveling with superluminal speed because it was emitted on the fourth day in a location that is in fast time and lower gravity. This light traveled through the space located between the quasar and the galaxy lens that imaged it in less than a day. The portion of the light wave that passes closest to or through the center of the galaxy lens slows more than the light farther out.

Both the light slowing down plus its bending by the lens are directly related to the strength of the gravitational field that was applied to the different portions of the light wave. The combined effects are observed on Earth as a stronger magnification than what the gravitational field of only the visible matter could produce if light speed remained constant.

This concept would negate one reason why scientists who support evolution invented dark matter. The observed effect is actually the proposed deceleration of light from superluminal speed caused by the visible matter's gravity rather than an increased gravity caused by more matter that cannot be seen in the focusing galaxy.

SUMMARY

By the end of fourth day, God completed the preparation of the expanse of the heavens and their hosts. On Day 1, he formed energy in the form of light and the atomic matter that emits and absorbs it. On Day 2, he prepared the heavens by separating the original fluid blob and forming the celestial spheres in their galaxies. On Day 4, he transformed the celestial spheres (proto-stars) into light providers all over the universe by igniting them. All the stars that resulted were unique in their brightness and color depending on their size and the atomic elements from which they formed. God used miracles of rapid maturing at each stage of their construction. Scientists who have developed evolutionary theories to explain the resulting universe have misconstrued these miracles. Their theories are based only on natural processes as observed on Earth. But they have found it necessary to add unknown forces, unknown matter, and unknown energy in their attempt to displace the one and only Creator.

God provided stars, planets, moons, and all the other hosts of the heavens in less than four days. Using supernatural miracles as he completed the universe, galaxies, and finally the solar system, God made the light of these luminaries arrive on Earth on the fourth day. This could have been done with superluminal light speeds and gravity warping of 4-D space-time. The effects of this warping are recorded in nature as drastically accelerated natural processes, perhaps by factors of millions or billions in the far off heavens. We speculated for the CM-model that even today light could travel much faster in deep space (away from any masses of atomic matter) than what has been measured here on Earth or even in our solar system. Hence, when astronomers look into the sky, they have observed events that took place on the fourth day when stars started providing their light. The events would have occurred in fast time and are replayed for the observer in the slower time of the region around Earth.

God also arranged the galaxy so that all the star systems in constellations move as a group at the same orbital speed so that the constellations remain similar in appearance for a long period of time. God arranged these stars into constellations for mankind to recognize and use as signs to determine direction and location on Earth's surface. They can also be used to measure the passage of a year here on Earth by their change in apparent position during Earth's orbit around the sun. God established Earth's rotation and orbit relative to the sun as the perpetual timekeeper for mankind to measure a day and a year, respectively. God established the motion of the moon relative to Earth and the sun to measure the seasons or months. All these products of God's sixth miracle were built to last until the end of time (Ps. 148:6). After he completed this divine act, it can be truly said that the heavens show the glory of God and the expanse shows his handiwork (Ps. 19:1).

CHAPTER 8

Summation of the Events in the Week of Creating and Making

DAYS 5–7: ANIMALS AND MANKIND
COMPLETE THE CREATED UNIVERSE

AFTER CREATING AND rapidly maturing the universe while preparing a perfect habitat on the surface of Earth in the first four days of the week, God began to fill the habitat with animals on the fifth day. He first formed the bodies and created life in the animals that swim and fly. Then on the sixth day, he did the same thing with land animals that walk and crawl on the ground. Finally, he formed and created mankind. God made such a large variety of animal kinds that there are perfectly suited inhabitants for every niche in the habitat he had prepared.

Every animal kind that God created and made showed many characteristics of having been intelligently designed and skillfully made. Furthermore, as the Ultimate Engineer, God reused his designs when a similar result was needed. The animals had the ability to move freely in their habitat. They were capable of sensing data in their environments, processing the data, and making decisions.

The complexity of the combination of the subsystems in the animal body has remained beyond human understanding. No robot has ever been designed or built that completely copies the wondrous designs found in even the simplest animals. Noticeably missing from robots are growth/repair and reproductive systems. These still hold the secrets that the super-intelligent Creator designed into them.

After completing all the animals, God created and made mankind in his own image. His final two miracles of creating and making on the sixth day resulted in the first two human beings. With these products of his divine actions, he completed his creating-and-making workweek. The final product was a perfectly formed and continually filling habitat for mankind to live in and serve their Creator. And it was originally designed and built to last forever. Then on the seventh day God rested.

SUMMATION OF EVENTS IN THE FIRST FOUR DAYS

The story of the events during the first four days of creation week that the author of the CMA reported is the only record mankind have of what took place prior to our own creation. If close attention is paid to what was recorded in those verses, the whole story of creating and rapid maturing of the universe unfolds. In this book, we described in modern terminology the divine actions that God used to make everything in the universe except animals and mankind in the first four days. The animals and mankind were created fully mature on the fifth and sixth days. We inferred from the CMA that the rapid maturing had ended on the fourth day so that natural events after that time would occur at a rate that the senses and minds of animals could comprehend.

In mankind's concept of the origins of the universe, the miracles that God commanded must take their prominent place. This was a progressive creating and making, which started with the basics of creating the location (heavens) and a universal substance (earth). After that initial miracle, God used a logical and well-designed sequence of miracles in making the entire physical universe. He may have used accelerated natural (that could be called supernatural) processes to transform the universal substance into everything but the consciousness and spirit of the animals and mankind. It all began when he created the initial items of time, space, and substance. In the following four days, he transformed, distributed, and arranged the substance into all the energy and matter that can now be observed in the physical universe.

In this book, we added reasonable speculations to fill in some details of the reported miracles that produced everything in the universe. But the author of the CMA provided the overall sequence and timeline of God's divine actions. The final product was a universe that was consistent with all the physical principles or laws that mankind have discovered. God's actions were logically sequenced and planned to fit his timeline for a six-day workweek and a seventh day for rest. They provided the model of a workweek for God's people, as recorded in Exodus 20:11: "For in six days the LORD made the heavens and the earth, the sea and all that is in them, and rested on the seventh day; therefore the LORD blessed the sabbath day and made it holy."

From a scientist's viewpoint, it should be difficult to ignore the intelligent design and skilled workmanship found in the created universe. From the smallest subatomic particle to the largest astronomical phenomenon, there is no lack of amazingly detailed design. Everything in the universe still operates well after more than six thousand years, and it performs within the Designer's constraints—the physical or natural laws. These laws did not naturally evolve or create themselves, but they were originally designed for, and imposed on, the creation by the Intelligent Designer and Creator, God.

Psalm 104 provided a short recap of the CMA with allusions to the events in the first four days of the creating-and-making week. We provide in the following paragraphs a more scientific version of that recap, taken from the chapters of this book.

Day 1

God started with his first miracle of creating from nothing a 4-D space-time containing the universal substance. This universal substance was a perfect fluid. It contained neither structure nor motion but included all the raw material that was required for God to make both. His second divine act focused on the perfect fluid from which he formed light and atomic matter. The products of this act were the tiny building blocks and strong mortar of the universe: atoms and the forces that hold them together. After forming the light, God established his time-measurement standard of a day by separating light from darkness.

The standard day was established as a period of relative darkness followed by a period of daylight.

Day 2

God's third miracle on the second day divided the blob of the resulting fluid matter into droplets and distributed them throughout the space he had created. The distributed fluids formed the large-scale structure of the universe. He first used dark clouds (possibly ultra-massive black holes) as transports for the atomic matter and stretched-out force fields between them to fill the far reaches of outer space. He then used supernatural winds and blazing fires (possibly white holes in the event horizons of the ultra-massive black holes) to distribute celestial spheres of very hot atomic matter into formations called galaxies. The celestial spheres became proto-stars, proto-planets, and spherical moons as they cooled down, depending on their composition of chemical elements, their size, and their location relative to each other. All of the spheres were separated from each other by space but were attracted to each other by the stretched-out force field called gravity.

Day 3

On the third day, God prepared the planet we call Earth, which has a single moon and is located in the solar system of a single star, as the place where he would locate his living creatures. He first flooded the surface of this planet with seawater and at the same time provided it with a thick atmosphere from reservoirs of liquids and gases formed within the amorphous crust of solidified rock. Then he raised at least one landmass made of granite to divide the surface into seas and dry ground. The dry ground was covered with dirt and sand made of rock that had been broken up by the tremendous forces of rushing water. The water ran off the rising ground and retreated to its sea basins. Springs of fresh water and dew from the atmosphere watered all the dry ground so plants could grow.

God's next divine action caused the ground to sprout all types of vegetation (both grasses and trees) that grew and reproduced their kinds. We speculated that he also caused all the plant-like organisms such as bacteria, protists, and fungi to sprout, grow, and reproduce their kinds. The single and multiple cells of vegetation and the plant-like organisms formed the basis of an ecosystem that provided food sources for all of God's living creatures.

Day 4

On the fourth day, God made the largest celestial spheres into stars that provided light for the universe, especially his chosen planet. He made the sun to rule the day and the moon that reflected its light to rule the night. He fixed the stars in the Milky Way galaxy in their locations in the sky so that they formed the visible constellations. Mankind have used these constellations as signs for direction on the Earth's surface and for telling the passage of time.

Conclusion

The author of the CMA recorded all of God's wondrous acts of creating and making the physical universe for mankind. The whole creation should praise the Lord for this (Ps. 148). A primary purpose of this book is to remind everyone of how the universe was brought into existence and to whom they owe their praise—the one and only Creator and Maker God, who was also the great Artist, Architect, Designer, Engineer, Intellect, Lover, etc. Praise be to Almighty God!

The Story of
Creating and Making

A S A PREFACE, allow us the freedom to set the stage for this story with a short fictional account of what could have happened on the evening of the eighth day of this created world in which mankind live. The sun has just set in the western sky to end the seventh day, on which God rested. Adam and Eve are still amazed at the world around them and are walking around exploring the garden called Eden. Suddenly Jesus is walking with them like he did with the two disciples on the road to Emmaus (Luke 24:13). He engages them in a conversation and they ask him the ultimate question of how this whole world came into existence. Jesus responds in his familiar manner with a story. This story paraphrases the creation and making account (CMA) found in the Bible as Gen 1:1–2:4a.

You can read that story below as interpreted by the author of this book. The reasons for the interpretation of the transliterated Hebrew words have been added below the paraphrased verses. This was done so that the meaning of the Hebrew words may not be lost in translation into the English language. The story is paraphrased but follows closely the New American Standard Bible translation of the first and part of the second chapter of Genesis.

Day 1—Genesis 1:1–5

1. In the beginning[1] we the Triune God [2] created[3] the pair of heavens[4] and the earth[5]. 2. The earth was formless[6] and void[7], and darkness[8] was over the surface[9] of the deep[10], and the Spirit of God was hovering over the surface of the fluid substance[11].

3. Then I, being the Word of God, said, "Let there be light[12]": and there was light. 4. We saw that the light was good; and we separated the light from the darkness.

5. We named the period of light day, and the period of darkness we named night[13]. And there was evening and there was morning, day one[14].

[1] The prepositional phrase "in the beginning" is adverbial and modifies the Hebrew verb. The Hebrew word translated "in the beginning" is *bereshiyth*. The *be-* prefix is translated as "in." The definite article "the" isn't in the Hebrew text, but its use in the English translation is justified because the Hebrew word *reshiyth* is a noun and there is only one created universe and it began at that one instant in time. The phrase tells the reader that God started his work of creating and making the world at the beginning of time.

[2] The Hebrew word translated "God" is *elohiym*. It is a noun constructed from three letters that form the root word *elh*. The suffix *-iym* identifies it as a masculine plural noun. The author uses this plural noun thirty-two times to designate the Creator God in this first chapter. The Scripture of the Old and New Testaments identifies him as the Triune God having three persons in one supreme being. We discover that all three persons of the Trinity were present during creation week from Malachi 2:10 (Father), Colossians 1:16 (Son), and Genesis 1:2 (Holy Spirit).

[3] The Hebrew word translated as "created" is *bara*. When this verb is used with *God* as the subject, it is defined as bringing something into existence from nothing that existed before (Heb. 11:3).

[4] The Hebrew word translated "heavens" is *shamayim*. It is always used in plural form with the special plural suffix *-yim* and always denotes more than one place. In the context of this verse, one of the places could have been the spiritual heaven, which is a place for the angels (1 Kings 22:19). It is also where God set up

his kingdom's throne and rules his creation (Ps. 103:19–22). It was not made from the earth and therefore has no physical structure or substance that makes it visible to mankind. Only spirits like God, his angels, and eventually the spirits of the saints can inhabit this place. The second heaven would have been the physical space-time continuum where God made the expanse and named it "the heavens" (Gen. 1:7–8). God later created a third heaven where God, the obedient angels, and saints will dwell for all eternity (2 Cor. 5:1; 12:2–4).

[5] The Hebrew word translated "earth" is *erets*. The word is a feminine noun and identifies the earth as the feminine part of the creation. This original earth was not a planet but a universal substance from which all physical things were later made. The earthen substance, as originally created, is described in the following verse.

[6] The Hebrew word translated "formless" is *tohu*. It is a masculine noun used as an adjective to describe the subject *earth*. It could have been used to denote that the original earthen substance was empty of basic structure such as atoms and did not have a recognizable shape.

[7] The Hebrew word translated "void" is *bohu*. It is also a masculine noun used as an adjective to describe the subject earth. It could have been used to denote that the original earthen substance was empty of motion or life. When God created marine life on the fifth day, he made it synonymous with motion (Gen. 1:20–21) and directed that living creatures should fill the void in their habitat on Earth (Gen. 1:22).

[8] The Hebrew word translated "darkness" is the masculine noun *choshek*. It is first used here when light didn't exist and again after light had been formed (Gen. 1:4). How God separated the light physically from the darkness (no or low light) is left for mankind to determine.

[9] The Hebrew phrase translated "over the surface" is *al paniym*. Since the noun is plural in the context of this verse, it denotes that the earthen substance had a surface facing every direction with total darkness extending above it.

[10] The Hebrew word translated "deep" is *tehom*. It is a noun that denotes a very deep place such as an abyss. The whole clause ending in this word is also adjectival and describes the subject earth. It tells the reader that the earthen substance had a surface, and it was very deep.

[11] The Hebrew word translated "fluid substance" is *mayim*. It is a special plural noun mostly translated as "waters" in the books of the Old Testament. But molecular water cannot exist without light, so here it is used to denote an unknown fluid substance. And, like the preceding clause, the clause ending in this word is also adjectival and describes the subject *earth*.

[12] The Hebrew word translated "light" is the feminine noun *owr*. The light is the first offspring of the original created earthen substance. According to Isaiah 45:7, God formed light, but he created the darkness. Light exists as electromagnetic radiation waves or particles (photons). When God saw something that was good, such as the light, it was formed perfectly and completely including everything physically related to it. In this case, the subatomic particles that make up all atomic matter were formed at the same time because they are sources and absorbers of light. Subatomic particles and light form a conversion pair so that it is physically possible to convert one into the other.

[13] God gave the Hebrew name *laylah* to the period of relative darkness that occurs every day after light was formed. It is a feminine noun translated "night" or "nighttime." In contrast, the time period when there is a majority of visible light each day was given the Hebrew name *yom*. It is a masculine noun meaning either "day" or "daytime." After light was formed, the darkness of nighttime that exists has never been devoid of all visible light. The term describes relative darkness rather than total darkness.

[14] The Hebrew words translated "day one" are *yom echad*. The full cycle day is here defined as starting in the evening and proceeding through the night, morning, and daytime and ending as the following evening begins. This was the time-period standard that God established for mankind, and he established it to last for all time.

Day 2—Genesis 1:6–8

6. Then on the evening of the second day I said, "Let there be expanse[1] in the midst[2] of the fluids, and let it separate[3] fluids from fluids." 7. We made the expanse and it separated the fluids which were beneath[4] the expanse from the fluids which were above in the expanse[5]; and it (the expanse) was established. 8. We named the expanse heaven(s)[6]. And there was evening and there was morning, a second day[7].

[1]   The Hebrew word translated "expanse" is the masculine noun *raqiya*. In the context of this verse, it denotes extraterrestrial space that separates all the celestial spheres from each other. The total space containing all the celestial spheres of earthen fluid is called "the expanse" *(haraqiya)* in verse 7.

[2]   The Hebrew word translated "midst" is *tavek*. In the context of this verse, it denotes that the space was interspersed between the separated drops of fluid in the universal blob of substance.

[3]   The Hebrew verb translated "separate" is *badal*. It actually describes the two actions of dividing a single item into two or more parts and then keeping the parts separated from each other. God did this by placing space between the drops of the divided fluids as he stretched out the heavens (Ps. 104:2).

[4]   The Hebrew word translated "beneath" is *tachath*. In the context of this verse, it denotes that the fluids that make up the celestial spheres form below the expanse.

[5]   The Hebrew phrase translated "above in the expanse" is *al leraqiya*. In the context of this verse, it denotes that the earthen fluids of a celestial sphere were separated from all the other celestial spheres in the expanse by space surrounding them.

[6]   Here God named the expanse "heavens" *(shamayim)*. This is the second use of the word and in the context of this verse denotes the stretched-out physical heavens that contained all the galaxies of celestial spheres in the universe. A different heaven is viewed in every direction from Earth.

[7]   This verse states that during the second day there was a period of nighttime and a period of daylight. We can only speculate that God used natural processes caused by supernatural

means for these nighttime and daytime periods, because the CMA doesn't report the source of light. Psalm 104 reported, alluding to the second day of creation week, that "He makes the [dark] clouds his chariot" (v. 3, paraphrased) and "flaming fire His ministers" (or "servants," v. 4, paraphrased). Somehow through these supernatural means God caused the darkness and daylight for the second day.

Day 3—Genesis 1:9–13

9. Then (on the evening of the third day) I said, "Let the waters below the heavens be gathered into one place[1], and let the dry land appear"[2]; and it (the surface of the Earth) was established. 10. We named the dry land earth[3], and the gathering of the waters We named seas[4]; and We saw that it (the sea and land surface) was good. 11. Then I said, "Let the earth sprout[5] vegetation[6], plants yielding seed, and fruit trees on the earth bearing fruit after their kind with seed in them": and it (the vegetation) was established. 12. The earth brought forth vegetation, plants yielding seed after their kind[7], and trees bearing fruit with seed in them, after their kind; and We saw that it (the vegetation) was good. 13. There was evening and there was morning, a third day[8].

[1] The Hebrew word translated "be gathered" is *qavah*. In the context of this verse, it denotes the gathering of seawater from many sources into one place. Job 38:8 reports, "When, bursting forth, it [the sea] went out from the womb." In other words, the sea was born within the Earth and poured out from under its surface. This divine act was also reported in Amos 5:8 and 9:6. Simultaneously, God "made a cloud its garment and thick darkness its swaddling band" (Job 38:9). This described the birth of the atmosphere that protected the seawater on the surface of the planet from the harsh conditions of extraterrestrial space.

[2] The Hebrew word translated "dry land" is *yabbashah*. It is used most frequently in the Bible to describe ground that has dried after being covered with water. Here it referred to a

landmass or continent having risen out of the seawater (per Ps. 104:7–9) on the Earth's surface. God then established the shores of the land as a boundary to the seas to keep the land dry (Prov. 8:29; Jer. 5:22).

[3] He named the dry land "earth." The dry land or earth contained atoms of all the chemical elements that exist in nature. These chemical elements were made from the original earthen fluid of verse 2 and now represent that universal substance.

[4] The Hebrew word translated "seas" is *yamiym*. In the context of this verse, it denotes actual molecular water that formed below the expanse. It first had gathered from reservoirs in the crust to cover the whole surface of the planet and when the landmass arose it ran off into basins (Ps. 104:6–9).

[5] The Hebrew verb translated "sprout" is *dasa*. It is used to describe how the vegetation originated in the ground and grew out of it.

[6] The Hebrew word translated "vegetation" is *deshe*. In the context of this verse, vegetation included all nonanimal organic material that grows and reproduces. Plant life formed the basis of Earth's ecosystem. The grasses and the fruit trees are two examples of vegetation that are reported in this verse. Microbes, algae, and fungi are examples of vegetation that were not mentioned.

[7] The Hebrew word translated "kind" is *miyn*. The biblical kind has no direct relationship with the modern categories of plants or animals, such as species. It referred to distinct original plants or animals. Since the third day, the original plant and animal kinds have produced all the variety of organisms through their seeds.

[8] Again, it is left to speculation what the source of the daylight was on the third day. One possibility is the burning of the dark atmospheric gases and particles that are described in Job 38:9. This could have cleared the skies for mankind's viewing of the hosts of heaven three days later.

Day 4—Genesis 1:14–19

14. Then [at the beginning of the fourth day] I said, "Let there be lights[1] in the expanse of the heavens to separate the day from the night, and let them be for signs and for seasons and for days and years; 15. and let them be for lights in the expanse of the heavens to give light on the earth": and it (lights in the heavens) was established. 16. We made the two great lights, the greater light to govern the day[2], and the lesser light to govern the night[3]; We made the stars[4] also. 17. We placed[5] them in the expanse of the heavens to give light on the earth, 18. and to govern the day and the night, and to separate the light from the darkness; and We saw that it (the completed heavens) was good. 19. There was evening and there was morning, a fourth day[6].

[1]   The Hebrew word translated "lights" is *ma'orot*. It is derived from the word for light *('owr)* and denotes the bearers or providers of light rather than light itself. A good translation would be "luminaries." They are the visible physical hosts of the heavens that include stars, planets, and moons.

[2]   The "greater light" that rules the daytime is the sun. There are three Hebrew words that are used later in the Old Testament to refer to the sun. *Cherec* is used in Job 9:7 to refer to the sun when it was commanded not to shine. *Shemesh* is used in Gen 15:12 to refer to the most brilliant object in the sky that sets in the west to mark the end of a day. *Chammah* is used in Psalm 19:6 to refer to the source of heat and light in a daily cycle for all the Earth. The sun has the three purposes of dividing the day and night, providing heat and light for the Earth, and marking the passage of time.

[3]   The moon is the "lesser light" that rules the nighttime. The Hebrew word used later in the Old Testament for the moon is *yareach* (Ps. 8:3). A closely related word, *yarach*, is sometimes translated "moon" but refers to the monthly cycle or phases of the moon.

[4]   The Hebrew word translated "stars" is *kokabiym*. The purposes of the stars are to provide light and act as signs. By the location of the stars, mankind can determine their direction of travel on

Earth, the change in seasons, and the length of a year. These signs are provided by the groupings of stars in the sky called constellations.

[5]   The Hebrew word translated "placed" is *nathan*. In the context of this verse, it denotes that the lights in the heavens were put into their relative positions so that they fulfilled their purposes.

[6]   The fourth day is the first day that the sun provided visible light to the Earth's surface. As such, it is a unique day because the beginning and ending of a day depended for the first time on a location on the surface of the planet. It is reasonable to speculate that the sun started shining on the evening of the fourth day when it would have set at the location of Eden. It is also reasonable to speculate that all the stars in the constellations became visible for mankind to see by the end of this same day.

Day 5—Genesis 1:20–23

20. Then [at the beginning of the fifth day] I said, "Let the waters teem with swarms[1] of living creatures[2], and let birds[3] fly above the earth in the open expanse of the heavens[4]." 21. We created the great sea monsters[5] and every living creature that moves (swims), with which the waters swarmed after their kind, and every winged flyer after its kind: and we saw that it (the swimming and flying animal kingdoms) was good. 22. I blessed them, saying, "Be fruitful and multiply, and fill the waters in the seas, and let the flyers multiply on the earth[6]." 23. There was evening and there was morning, a fifth day.

[1]   The Hebrew word translated "teem" is the verb *sharats*, and the word translated "swarms" is *sherets*, a noun. In the context of verses 20–21, swarms could denote schools of fish, pods of whales, and any other groups of aquatic animals. The aquatic animals that are described in these verses spend most of their life swimming in water.

[2]   The Hebrew words translated "living creatures" are *nephesh chayh*. Literally translated it would read "that which breathes

its life." In the Bible, only animals and mankind are considered living creatures. The life of an animal is in its blood, according to Leviticus 17:11. Oxygen is the life-giving substance unique to the blood and breath of animals. Plants don't carry oxygen in the sap; they expel it rather than breathe it in and therefore are not considered living creatures.

[3]   The Hebrew word translated "birds" is *owph*. It can be used in general to refer to any flying creature with wings, including birds, reptiles, mammals, and insects.

[4]   The Hebrew phrase translated "in the open expanse of the heavens" is *al paniym raqiya hashamayim*. Literally translated it would read "over the faces of the expanse of the heavens." The day and night skies as seen from the surface of Earth were the two faces of the expanse. Later, when clouds formed in the sky, the faces of the expanse changed in number from two to many.

[5]   The Hebrew word translated "sea monsters" is *tanniyniym*. The context of this verse allows it to denote large sea mammals like whales or large sea reptiles like sea serpents, dragons, or even dinosaurs that live a majority of the time partially or fully submerged in water.

[6]   This sentence is a directive from God for the animals to reproduce their kind through the seed they had been given. Only living creatures were given this directive, because they have a consciousness created in their bodies known as the mind. Plants filled their niches in the ecosystem automatically when they sprouted from the earth. The plants were biblically nonliving organisms, and they did not have a mind. Therefore they did not need a directive from God to reproduce.

Day 6—Genesis 1:24–31

24. Then [at the beginning of the sixth day] I said, "Let the earth bring forth living creatures after their kind: cattle[1] and creeping things[2] and beasts of the earth[3] after their kind": and it (the land-animal kingdom) was established. 25. We made the beasts of the earth after their kind, and the cattle after their kind, and everything that creeps on the ground after its kind: and We saw that it (the land-animal kingdom) was good.

26. Then I said, "Let Us make man[4] in Our image[5], according to Our likeness[6]; and let them rule over the fish of the sea and over birds of the sky and over the cattle and over all the earth, and over every creeping thing that creeps on the earth[7]." 27. We created you in Our own image, in the image of God We created you; [both] male and female We created you. 28. (I'm sure you remember) We blessed you; and I said to you, "Be fruitful and multiply, and fill the earth, and subdue it; and rule over the fish of the sea and over the birds of the sky and over every living thing that moves on the earth."

29. Then I (also) said, "Behold[8], I have given you every plant yielding seed that is on the surface of all the earth, and every tree which has fruit yielding seed; it shall be food for you; 30. and to every beast of the earth and to every bird of the sky and to everything that moves on the earth which has life, I have given every green plant for food[9]": and it (the whole land-animal ecosystem) was established. 31. We saw everything that We had made, and behold, it (the whole creation) was very[10] good. And there was evening and there was morning, the sixth day.

[1]   The Hebrew word translated "cattle" is *behemah*. In the context of this verse, it denotes all kinds of quietly grazing land animals.

[2]   The Hebrew word translated "creeping things" is *remes*. In the context of this verse, it denotes all the smaller animals that move with feet on the ground. These animals could include rodents, reptiles, and nonflying insects.

[3]   The Hebrew phrase translated "beasts of the earth" is *chayhu erets*. Literally translated, it means "land animals." In the context of this verse, it denotes all the wild land animals not included in the previous two categories mentioned.

[4]   The Hebrew word translated "man" is *adam*. In the next sentence, the word is used to include all mankind, both male and female, therefore denoting mankind. The separate creation of a man and then a woman is described in Genesis 2:7, 21–22.

[5]   The Hebrew word translated "image" is *tselem*. Mankind were designed as both physically living beings and spiritual reflections of God. They would have lived forever on Earth in a paradise if they had not sinned.

[6] The Hebrew word translated "likeness" is *demut*. In the context of this verse, it denotes mankind's role as God's physical representatives on Earth.

[7] God gave his physical representative on Earth a directive to rule over all the other living creatures and to make use of the dry land to grow plants for his food.

[8] The Hebrew word translated "behold" is *hinneh*. In the context of this verse, it was a directive from God for man to look around and see all the varieties of vegetation God had provided for him as food.

[9] Notable by their absence from this list of animals are the aquatic animals or swimmers. We must assume that God had made separate provisions for their ecosystem to function perfectly to supply their needs. Even today many aquatic animals live on algae and marine organisms called plankton that can be considered plant-like life.

[10] The Hebrew word translated "very" is *meod*. It denotes that the whole universe, including the human habitat on Earth and all its creatures, was entirely perfect as God completed it in the previous six days.

Day 7—Genesis 2:1–4

1. Thus[1] the heavens and the earth were completed, and all their hosts[2]. 2. By the seventh day We had completed[3] Our work and We rested[4] on the seventh day from all Our work which We had done. 3. Then We blessed the seventh day and sanctified[5] it, because in it We rested from all Our work which We had created and made. 4. This is (My) account[6] of the heavens and the earth when they were created.

[1] The Hebrew word for "thus" is not in the original text. It most likely was the result of adding chapter designations. It seems to be used to tie the beginning of the second chapter to the end of the first. This verse in the original text begins like most before it with the Hebrew word *waw* that is mostly translated as either "and" or "then."

[2] The Hebrew phrase translated "all their hosts" is *kol tsabam*. It most likely denotes every kind of host that had been created. There are the hosts of the spiritual heavens—the angels; the hosts of the physical heavens—the luminaries; and the hosts living on the Earth—the animals and mankind.

[3] The Hebrew word translated "completed" is *kalah*. In the context of this verse, it denotes the completion of God's work at the end of the sixth day with the creating and making of mankind.

[4] The Hebrew word translated "rested" is *shabath*. This is a verb that denotes ceasing work. The Hebrew noun *shabbath* is derived from this word, and the English word "sabbath" followed from it.

[5] The Hebrew word translated "sanctified" is *qadash*. In the context of this verse, it denotes God setting the seventh day apart and making it a holy day dedicated to him. It was to be observed as a day of rest by the Israelites after the giving of the law to Moses at Mount Sinai (Ex. 20:10).

[6] The Hebrew word translated "account" is *toledot*. This verse ends the account of the creating and making of the universe. This word is used to identify a total of ten accounts that make up the book of Genesis. This first account is the only one that is not ascribed to a patriarch and therefore points to its divine author. The other nine uses of the word are found in Genesis 5:1, 6:9, 10:1, 11:10, 11:27, 25:19, 36:1, 36:9, 37:2.

Once Jesus had finished this story, we can assume he asked Adam and Eve to pass it down to all their descendents. It still survives today because God took a special interest in making this story available to all of mankind through his prophet Moses. In this manner it has been passed down to all of Adam's descendants throughout the thousands of years that the world has existed.

Endnotes

The books and Web sites cited in these notes are accessible to a general audience; the journal articles referred to are usually original scientific works and are marked with an asterisk (*) to indicate a technical reference.

Chapter 2

1. Alex Williams and John Hartnett, *Dismantling the Big Bang* (Green Forest, AR: Masters Books, 2005).
2. Robert Leighton, *Principles of Modern Physics* (New York: McGraw-Hill, 1959).
3. *Riordan, M., and W. A. Zaic, "The First Few Microseconds," *Scientific American* 294(5):34A–39, 2006.
4. *James Lattimer and Madappa Prakash, "The Physics of Neutron Stars," *Science* 304(5670):536–542, 2004.
5. *Pavel K. Kovtun, Dam T. Son, and Andrei O. Starinets, "Viscosity in Strongly Interacting Quantum Field Theories from Black Hole Physics," *Physics Review Letters* 94:111601–111609, 2005.
6. D. Russell Humphreys, *Starlight and Time.* (Green Forest, AR: Masters Books, 1994).

Chapter 3

1. Ralph Alpher and Robert Herman, *Genesis of the Big Bang* (New York: Oxford University Press, 2001).
2. *Rik J. Williams, et al., "Probing the Local Group Medium toward Mkn 421 with *Chandra* and *FUSE*," *Astrophysics Journal* 631: 856–867, 2005.
3. *Geoffrey C. Bower, et al., "Detection of the Intrinsic Size of Sagittarius A* Through Closure Amplitude Imaging," *Science* 304(5671):704–708, 2004.
4. *Ramesh Narayan and Eliot Quataert, "Black Hole Accretion," *Science* 307(5706):77–80, 2005.
5. *M. Coleman Miller, Christopher S. Reynolds, and Anita Krishnamurthi, "Supermassive Black Holes: Shaping Their Surroundings," *Sky & Telescope* 109(4):43–47, 2005.

Chapter 4

1. Greg S. Jorgensen, "The canopy, the Moon, the tilt of the Earth's Axis, and a pre-flood ice age" in Robert E Walsh, Ed., *The Proceedings of the Third International Conference on Creationism* (Pittsburgh: Creation Science Fellowship, 1994), 287–293.
2. Humpheys, *Starlight and Time.*
3. Halton Arp, *Seeing Red.* (Montreal: Apeiron, 1998).
4. Edward A. Boudreaux, "Origin of Chemical Elements, Appendix," in Lawrence Vardiman, et al. *Radioisotopes and the Age of the Earth, Volume I.* (Chino Valley, AZ: Institute for Creation Research, El Cajon and Creation Research Society, 2000), 622–625.
5. *Williams, et al. "Probing the Local Group Medium," 856–867.
6. *Ron Samec, "No sign of gravitational lensing in cosmic microwave background," *Journal of Creation* 20(2):3, 2006.
7. Arp, *Seeing Red.*
8. Andrew A. Snelling, "Radiohalos in Granites: Evidence for accelerated nuclear decay," in Lawrence Vardiman, et al. *Radioisotopes and the Age of The Earth, Volume II*, ch 3: 101–207.
9. Donald B. DeYoung, *Thousands . . . Not Billions* (Green Forest, AR: Master Books, 2005).

10. Guillermo Gonzalez and Jay Richards, *The Privileged Planet: The Search For Purpose in the Universe* (Washington DC, Regnery Publishing, 2004).
11. Arp, *Seeing Red*.

Chapter 5

1. *D. Russell Humphreys, "The Earth's Magnetic Field is Still Losing Energy," *Creation Research Society Quarterly* 39:3–13, 2002.
2. *Motohiko Murakami, et al., "Water in Earth's lower mantle," *Science*, 295, 1885–1887, 2002.
3. Joseph Silk, *The Big Bang* (San Francisco, W. H. Freeman and Co, 1980).
4. *Christina L. De La Rocha, "Palaeoceanography: In hot water," *Nature* 443: 920–921, 26 Oct 2006.
5. DeYoung, *Thousands . . . Not Billions*.
6. *Anthony Kemp, et al., "Magmatic and Crustal Differentiation History of Granitic Rocks from Hf-O Isotopes in Zircon," *Science* 315: 980, 2007.
7. *John M. Eiler, "On the Origins of Granites," *Science* 315, 951, 2007.
8. *John W. Valley, "A Cool Early Earth?" *Scientific American* 33, 59, 2005.
9. DeYoung, *Thousands . . . Not Billions*.
10. *Gabriel Tobie, Jonathan I. Lunine and Christophe Sotin, "Episodic outgassing as the origin of atmospheric methane on Titan," *Nature* 440: 61–64, 2 March 2006.
11. *Wendy L. Mao, Carolyn A. Koh, and E. Dendy Sloan, "Clathrate hydrates under pressure," *Physics Today*, 60(10): 42–47, 2007.

Chapter 6

1. George Johnson, *The Living World*. (Boston: McGraw-Hill Higher Education, 2000).
2. Duane T. Gish, *Evolution: The Fossils Still Say No!* (El Cajon, CA: Institute for Creation Research, 1995).

3. *Jonathan Sarfati, "Green Power: God's solar power plants amaze chemists," *Technical Journal* 19(1):14–15, 2005.
4. Johnson, *The Living World.*
5. *David Demick, "The molecular sledgehammer," *Creation Magazine* 24(2):52–53, March 2002.
6. *Dan Cullen, "Fungal symbiosis unearthed," *Nature* 452:42–43, 6 March 2008.
7. *Wayne P. Armstrong, "The Yucca and Its Moth," *Zoonooz* Vol 72 (4): 28-31, April 1999. A modified version of this article can be found at http://waynesword.edu/ww0902a.htm (accessed 16 July 2011)

Chapter 7

1. Donald B. DeYoung, *Astronomy and the Bible* (Grand Rapids: Baker Books, 2000).
2. Barry Setterfield, *Proceedings of the Cosmology Conference 2003, Session 6* (Columbus, OH: Creation Research, Science Education Foundation, 2003).
3. Humphreys, *Starlight and Time.*
4. Danny Faulkner, *Universe by Design* (Green Forest, AR: Master Books, 2004).
5. *John D. Anderson, Philip A. Laing, Eunice L. Lau, Anthony S. Liu, Michael Martin Nieto and Slava G. Turyshev, "Study of the anomalous acceleration of Pioneer 10 and 11," *Physics Review D* 65:082004, 2002.
6. *D. Russell Humphreys, "Creationist cosmologies explain the anomalous acceleration of Pioneer spacecraft," *Journal of Creation* 21(2): 61–70, 2007.
7. *Bill Worraker, "MOND over dark matter?" *Technical Journal* 16(3): 11–14, 2002.
8. *D. Russell Humphreys, "Our galaxy is the centre of the universe, 'quantized' red shifts show," *Technical Journal* 16(2): 1–10, 2002.
9. *Leon V. E. Koopmans and Roger D. Blandford, "Gravitational Lenses," *Physics Today* 57(6): 45–51, 2004.

Index

Index

R

radiance 145–146
radiohalos 74–75
radio, radio-wave radiation 18
radioisotopes 60, 74
radius 20, 30, 34, 41–42, 65, 156
raging infernos 51
rain 47, 105, 136
rate of change 7, 24, 31, 41, 56, 95, 125, 156–165
red giant (star) 146, 148
red oak 128
redshift 149, 158–161, 167
RedShift-Distance method (RSD) 159
reduction 135, 163
Relativistic Heavy Ion Collider 21
relativity, general (GR) 15, 49, 55, 167
relativity, special 14
reproductive process 118, 128, 131, 171
reservoirs 81, 85, 91, 98, 111–112, 174
rhizobium, bacteria 135–136
rhyolite 88, 94–96
ribonucleic acid (RNA) 121
ripe almonds 117
robotic system 133, 158
roots 117, 125–126, 135–137
rosettes 137

S

salts 87
sandstone 89
satellite 44, 110
Saturn 100, 106, 110,
scientific terminology 1, 4, 12, 13, 29, 54, 87, 119, 146
seas 81–83, 85–87, 92, 94, 103, 112, 115
seasons 125, 136, 143, 150, 152, 170
seawater 80–83, 85–88, 90–97, 105–107, 112
second day 40–41, 50–54, 58–62, 66–70, 92, 101
sediment 81, 89, 93, 96–97, 105–108, 112

sedimentary rock 88–89, 97–98, 107–109, 112
seeds 116, 122–127, 129–130, 134, 138
self-sustaining ecosystem 124, 126
senses 172
sensing data 171
separated 38–41, 47–51, 53–54, 58, 61, 74, 79
servants 52
sexual reproduction 129–131, 135
shadow 39–40, 72
shorelines, land/sea boundaries 83, 94
shrubs 137
silicon dioxide, quartz 89, 106–107
silicon–based compounds 90
sin 119
single-celled 119–120, 127, 135–136, 139
slow time 158
snapshot 28, 49–53
solid 30, 56–57, 67–69, 73–75, 87–92, 99
solution 41, 55, 157, 163
space warping 158, 160
space-time continuum, 4–D 15, 17, 23, 25, 34, 36, 44, 57
spectrum, range of EMR frequencies 15–18, 23, 32, 36, 38–39, 71–72, 143
speculation 2, 17–19, 23, 26, 58, 67, 74, 134,155
speed of light, c 15, 41–42, 66, 103, 155–158, 167–168
spiral galaxy 63, 101, 165
spores 123
spreading out 47, 52, 54, 112
springs, water 81, 85–86, 92, 94, 106, 112, 124, 174
sprout 93, 115, 117–127, 129, 137–139, 150
spruce 130
stamen 134
Standard Model 13, 21

CPSIA information can be obtained at www.ICGtesting.com
Printed in the USA
BVOW020343301112

306845BV00002B/4/P